METHUEN'S MONOGRAPHS
ON BIOLOGICAL SUBJECTS

———

General Editor

KENNETH MELLANBY

CYTOLOGICAL TECHNIQUE
The Principles underlying Routine Methods

Cytological Technique

THE PRINCIPLES UNDERLYING
ROUTINE METHODS

———

JOHN R. BAKER

D.Sc.(Oxon.), F.R.S.

Reader in Cytology in the University of Oxford
Joint Editor of the
Quarterly Journal of Microscopical Science

LONDON: METHUEN & CO LTD

NEW YORK: JOHN WILEY & SONS INC

First published 1933
Second edition, rewritten 1946
Third edition 1950
Fourth edition, rewritten 1960
Reprinted 1963
Printed and bound in Great Britain
by Butler & Tanner Ltd, Frome and London

CATALOGUE NO (METHUEN) 2/4101/11

4.2

Dedicated
to the Memory of

GILBERT C. BOURNE, F.R.S.

Preface

A quarter of a century has passed since the first edition of this book was published. During that period cytology has been transformed. Seldom has any branch of science been so revolutionized in a similar period by the invention of new techniques and the revival of old ones. The subject-matter of the *Cytological Technique* of 1933 is only a little fraction of the cytological technique we know today. Nevertheless, the old processes of fixation, embedding, dyeing, and mounting survive and flourish. Indeed, it seems probable that even hundreds of years hence they will still be necessary. Perhaps some cytologist of the distant future, looking through the books on a forgotten shelf in the basement of an old library, will read these words and agree that I was not mistaken.

The old title of the earlier editions is retained at the special request of the Publishers. The newer branches of the subject are being covered in Biological Monographs written by other authors. Dr W. G. B. Casselman's book on *Histochemical Technique*[53] has already been published, and another by Dr J. Chayen on biophysical methods is in course of preparation.

The earlier editions have been subjected to the sincerest form of flattery, for considerable parts have been taken from them and reprinted in text-books with scarcely any change, and usually without acknowledgement; and the Chinese have done me the honour of pirating the whole book and producing it in their own characters. All this is very encouraging and suggests that the underlying plan was good. So, although this new edition has been rewritten from start to finish, without the copying of a single sentence, yet I have followed the original plan. That is to say, I have chosen as few and as simple techniques as possible, and have used them as illustrations of general principles.

Although this new edition is concerned primarily with the principles rather than the practice of microtechnique, I have thought it right to come down to earth occasionally by giving detailed practical instructions. The intention is to show the student some of the applications of the principles. No attempt is made, however, to provide a consecutive course of instruction in practical microtechnique, for there are many excellent text-books devoted to this subject.[48, 85, 143, 105, 148, 161]

When the first edition was written, I had already given nine annual courses in microtechnique to students of zoology at Oxford. Since then I have given twenty-four more. If one keeps up with progress in a particular subject over a long period, it becomes increasingly difficult to write a short book about it. One can scarcely make a single statement without thinking of exceptions and reservations, or being conscious that an accurate exposition would require longer treatment. The temptation to equivocate is strong, but must be resisted. It will be realized that my object is to transmit a general grasp of the subject—to put the reader in a position to understand the complications when he or she comes up against them.

I hope that some readers may decide to pursue the subject further in my larger book, *Principles of Biological Microtechnique* (1958).[21] Those who have already seen the *Principles* may wonder whether there is anything in the present book that might interest them. The chief subject that is better treated here, I believe, is the action of mordants. I have been carrying out research on this since I wrote the *Principles*. I think it may be claimed that Chapter 9 of this book includes the first attempt to present a consistent theory of mordanting in microtechnique, though certain parts of the process have been admirably treated by Wigglesworth[185] and others. Much is known about the use of basic chromium salts as mordants for azo-dyes in the textile industry, but this is a radically different process. The discussion on fixative mixtures contains a number of new ideas. There is also a clearer account of fixation by mercuric chloride. In addition, the present book deals with three subjects—embedding, mounting, and the structure of the cell—that are only mentioned incidentally in the other.

In this new edition I must mention again the benefit I have derived from the practical assistance of Mrs B. M. Luke (formerly Miss Jordan) over a period of many years. Mrs J. A. Spokes has once more typewritten the whole book and helped me by careful attention to detail throughout. Several colleagues have given me valuable advice on particular problems. I must especially thank Dr E. L. Bowen, Mr F. M. Brewer, Mr W. Llowarch, and above all Dr L. M. Venanzi, who has generously put his knowledge of the chemistry of aluminium at my disposal. Any errors must be attributed to myself alone, for my advisers have not seen what I have written. Sir Alister Hardy has continued to support cytological studies in the Department of Zoology at Oxford, and it is a pleasure to acknowledge his help.

JOHN R. BAKER

Cytological Laboratory
Department of Zoology
University Museum
Oxford

The reprinting of this book has given the opportunity to correct a few minor slips. I must also mention that I have changed my opinion about the Golgi apparatus (pp. 3 and 10). For a full statement of my present views on this subject the reader is referred to a paper entitled 'New developments in the Golgi controversy', which will be published shortly in the *Journal of the Royal Microscopical Society*.

JOHN R. BAKER
August 1963

Contents

Illustrations

Abbreviations

aq   aqueous (solution)
cm   centimetre(s)
DNA   deoxypentose nucleic acid
g   gram(s)
ml   millilitre(s)
mm   millimetre(s)
μ micron(s)
mμ millimicron(s)
o.p.   oxidation potential
RNA   ribonucleic acid
v/v   expresses the concentration of a solute in terms of the number of ml of the solute in 100 ml of the solution.
w/v   expresses the concentration of a solute in terms of the number of g of the solute in 100 ml of the solution.
w/w   expresses the concentration of a solute in terms of the number of g of the solute in 100 g of the solution.
w/W   expresses the concentration of a solute in terms of the number of g of the solute in 100 g of the solvent.

In this book the concentrations of liquid solutes are expressed as v/v. Thus 5% acetic acid means a solution containing 5 ml of the acid in each 100 ml of solution.

The concentrations of solid and gaseous solutes are expressed as w/v, except where the contrary is stated. Thus 4% formaldehyde means a solution containing 4 g of the gas in each 100 ml of solution.

CHAPTER 1

The Structure of the Cell

This book deals with the scientific principles underlying some of the most ordinary processes of biological microtechnique: that is to say, with the fixation, embedding, dyeing, and mounting of small parts of organisms for subsequent study under the microscope. It deals chiefly with the preparation of material for light-microscopy; indeed, dyeing is not applicable if cells are to be examined with the electron-microscope (p. 85).

The purpose of ordinary microscopical preparations is to reveal minute structure. The study of this structure shows that most organisms consist of cells and intercellular (or extra-cellular) material; objects formed by the transformation of cells (the red blood-corpuscles of mammals, for instance) often constitute a third category of components.[13] The primary components are the cells, because the other constituents of the tissues do not appear in their absence. The cells are, in fact, the *proto-plasm*[153, 129] or *first-formed* material, as indeed we can tell by examining an early embryo; but since the expression *first-formed* may suggest that something else formed them, it is more logical to say that they are the *plasson* or formative material.[89] The plasson constitutes the subject-matter of cytology, and this book is concerned primarily (though not exclusively) with its fixation and after-treatment in the routine processes of microtechnique.

It would be a convenience if one could describe a 'typical cell' and then show how this object was affected by the ordinary processes of microtechnique. Unfortunately there is in reality no such object, though pictures of it appear in various textbooks. Cells show great diversity of structure in relation to their particular functions. Some are so obviously untypical that they could not possibly serve as representatives of other kinds. Extremes of this sort are the flagellate spermatozoon, with strongly marked polarity and scarcely any ground cytoplasm, and the ovum, with a most unusual spherical or ovoid form and nearly always with masses of reserve food-material preventing a clear view of the other cytoplasmic inclusions. Embryonic cells are more unspecialized. Those of animals are usually epithelial and mesenchymatous; and since the latter are derived from the former, a case can be made for the selection of an embryonic epithelial cell as typical of cells in general. In fact, however, such cells usually contain yolk granules, and these are much more evident than the cytoplasmic inclusions that occur regularly in cells of all kinds. The primary meristematic cells of plants are more unspecialized than the embryonic cells of animals, and might indeed have been selected for our purpose.

Animals do not maintain many reserve stores of unspecialized cells, but rather produce new cells, when required, by the multiplication of those that have already become specialized for particular purposes. Spermatogonia and oogonia, however, do constitute reserve stores of unspecialized cells, and an examination of them will reveal what parts are necessary for the retention of life itself, as opposed to the performance of special functions on behalf of the organism as a whole. An ordinary spermatogonium may be regarded as more or less typical of the unspecialized cells of animals, and it will serve here as an approximation to the ideal 'typical cell'. We shall see later how its structure is altered artificially by many of the usual processes of microtechnique.

To determine the structure of a cell, it is essential to examine it first while it is still alive. It can be examined in a body-fluid or in a saline solution of appropriate osmotic pressure. The cell must be examined in its unaltered state by phase-contrast microscopy, and also by direct microscopy after the use of vital dyes. Subsequently it is proper to try every method of microtechnique that can reasonably be supposed to throw light on the living structure.

The first thing to notice is the shape of the cell. Spermatogonia do not maintain a particular form by the secretion of a solid cell-wall. Their boundaries are usually determined by the pressure of neighbouring cells and other tissue-constituents. They often occur in cysts filled with similar cells. The external cells lie against the wall of the cyst, but the others may be bounded by cells similar to themselves. Mutual pressure gives a characteristic shape to each cell. It has many sub-equal sides. These are nearly flat, except where a cell abuts on the curved wall of the cyst or tubule that contains the cells, or projects freely into the central cavity. In section, most of the spermatogonia therefore appear polygonal (fig. 1). The cell-membrane is exceedingly thin, far below the limit of measurement by the light-microscope; but whether we can actually see a cell-membrane or not in any particular cell, we are compelled by convincing evidence to postulate the existence of a thin surface layer having different characters from the material within.

Beneath the cell-membrane lies the ground cytoplasm with its inclusions. Spermatogonia commonly contain five kinds of cytoplasmic inclusions that are large enough to be seen with the light-microscope. Three of these appear to be invariably present in ordinary cells. They do not occur in mature red blood-corpuscles of mammals, and all of them do not occur in all spermatozoa; but they are present in young red blood-corpuscles and also in spermatids, which are young spermatozoa. The three kinds of cytoplasmic inclusions that are present in spermatogonia and in all ordinary cells are the nucleus, mitochondria, and lipid globules.

It may be thought degrading to the dignity of the nucleus to call it a cytoplasmic inclusion, but logic seems to demand that it should be included under this head. Some authorities would list the 'Golgi apparatus' as a regular constituent of cells, but this name appears to have been given to a variety of different objects, not falling into a single category.[167, 112, 100, 15, 170, 171, 19, 55, 56, 133, 22, 113] (See, however, p. ix.)

Spermatogonia commonly contain two other kinds of cytoplasmic inclusions, which are of frequent but not universal occurrence in cells. These are the centriole and idiozome.

The five kinds of cytoplasmic inclusions will now be briefly

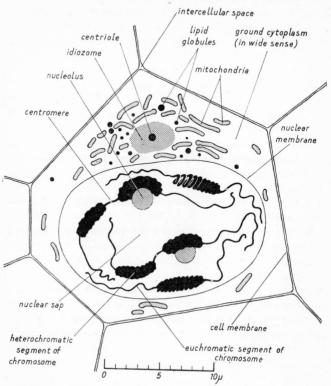

Fig. 1. A typical spermatogonium, seen in optical section. The figure is intended to show the structure of the living cell. Compare with fig. 4, p. 26. (The contents of the nucleus are represented diagrammatically; the rest of the figure is based on the spermatogonium of the common newt, Triturus vulgaris.*)*[24]

considered. The nucleus will be taken first, but it will be convenient to describe the rest of the inclusions in a different order from that given above, mainly because the idiozome is such a striking object in typical spermatogonia.

The nucleus is the largest single cytoplasmic inclusion in most cells. In spermatogonia it is commonly eccentric (fig. 1), and this confers polarity on the cell, which is radially symmetrical about a linear axis (though there is no precise symmetry of the flat sides). The eccentricity of the nucleus leaves the bulk of the cytoplasm at one end of the cell, and the idiozome lies near the middle of this cytoplasmic mass. The nucleus of spermatogonia is usually ovoid or spherical, but sometimes concave on the side towards the idiozome. This concavity towards the idiozome is not unusual in various cells, especially certain leucocytes. The nucleus is bounded by a distinct membrane, but this is too thin to show any structure with the light-microscope.

The nucleus contains spherical or subspherical bodies called nucleoli. These commonly appear after mitosis, close up against certain particular parts of particular chromosomes. Since the latter are present in the form of two equal sets, the nucleoli are usually present at first in equal numbers; but they have a tendency to fuse, and many cells contain only one. The nucleoli are particularly dense, heavy objects.[91] When a cell disintegrates after death, the nucleoli and lipid droplets are distinguishable after everything else has disappeared. Nucleoli contain basic proteins and ribonucleic acid (RNA), and also, apparently, some phospholipid. They are usually largest in cells that are actively synthesizing protein in the cytoplasm, but no satisfactory explanation of this fact has been produced.

Our knowledge of the structure of the part of the nucleus not occupied by the nucleoli is unfortunately meagre. The electron-microscope has given little help towards the solution of this problem. Some authorities consider that during the late stages of telophase the chromosomes swell until they touch one another; others think that they spin out as thin threads that are separated from one another by a continuous fluid or weak gel, the nuclear sap. It is probable that both kinds of nuclei exist, but the weight of evidence seems to suggest that in most cells the chromosomes are largely in the form of very long, thin threads, not distinctly visible with the light-microscope and not colourable by the dyes that attach themselves so intensely to the mitotic chromosomes. The whole of each chromosome, however, is not present in this form, for certain particular regions, called the heterochromatic segments or karyosomes, do not undergo the same telophase transformations as the rest, but remain as thick, somewhat irregular bodies, easily visible in the living cell. The hetero-chromatic segments are colourable without difficulty in fixed preparations, since they contain deoxypentosenucleic acid (DNA), which is the main substance responsible for the fact that the mitotic chromosomes are so easily dyed. DNA has a strong affinity for all members of the large group of colouring agents known as basic dyes (p. 90).

DNA is not confined to the heterochromatic segments, but appears to be distributed throughout the whole of the rest of the nucleus (apart from the nucleolus), at a lower concentration than in the heterochromatic segments.[144] The form in which it is distributed is not known. Possibly it is strung out along the fine threads that constitute the normal or euchromatic segments of the chromosomes; possibly these threads are at this stage com-posed of protein only, and the DNA is in colloidal solution in the nuclear sap.

Before the chromosomes reappear distinctly in early prophase, they have split longitudinally throughout their length. It is not known exactly when this splitting occurred, and an arbitrary decision must therefore be reached as to whether the chromosomes should be represented in a diagram as split or unsplit. They are represented in fig. 1 as single threads, swollen in particular places into heterochromatic segments. Only two pairs of chromosomes are represented in the diagram, but in the great majority of animals the diploid number exceeds ten.

In dyed preparations of cells undergoing mitosis, each chromo-some appears to be interrupted at a particular spot, where there is a short segment lacking affinity for basic dyes. This segment is the spindle-attachment or centromere. Long chromosomes are attached to the spindle by this body, but short ones are wholly embedded in the spindle. The centromere is the part of the chromosome that leads the rest in the movement towards the centriole in early anaphase. Since each centromere occupies an unvarying position in each chromosome, it presumably persists from telophase to the succeeding prophase.

During interphase, the centriole may often be distinguished near the middle of the mass of cytoplasm situated at the opposite pole of the cell from the nucleus. This body is too small for the light-microscope to reveal any structure in it. Astral rays and one end of the spindle were centred on it at the preceding division. We have no proof that it always persists from one cell-division to the next. Shortly before the next division two centrioles are present, close to each other.

The centriole is surrounded by a subspherical but rather irregularly-shaped body. This was named *Idiozom*,[121] because it forms a special envelope round the centriole (Greek *ídios*, special; *zōma*, envelope). The word may be written 'idiozome' in English, but it is wrong to spell it with an *s* in place of a *z*, though this is often done.[156] It is difficult to see in the untreated, living cell, but in some cases it can be made evident by the use of vital dyes (neutral red, dahlia). It appears structureless when examined by the light-microscope, and no definite limiting membrane can be seen. It is present continuously from one cell-division to the next, whether the centriole persists or not. The chemical composition of the idiozome has not been worked out fully. It is not so markedly different from the rest of the cytoplasm in chemical composition as to be readily dyed in a contrasting colour. It has, however, a somewhat greater affinity for the colouring agents called 'acid' dyes (p. 90). If a suitably fixed testis is soaked in a solution of osmium tetroxide, the latter is reduced at its surface to produce a deposit of the black hydrated dioxide. The idiozome corresponds with what some authors have called the centrosome, but it is probably best to avoid this word, since it has been applied also to the centriole. The functional significance of the idiozome remains obscure.

In many kinds of cells, especially blastomeres, there is a body showing general resemblance to the idiozome, but the astral rays of the preceding mitosis persist in continuity with it, so that it appears spiky; it is commonly granular. This body in blastomeres was at first regarded as constituting the essential part of the protoplasm: indeed, the name protoplasm was sometimes restricted to the material of this particular object.[40] The word

Archoplasma was coined later to indicate the distinction between this material and the rest of the protoplasm.[41] It seems probable that the archoplasm of blastomeres corresponds to the idiozome of spermatogonia and other cells, though this has been denied.[71]

Sinuous rods or threads are seen in all parts of the cytoplasm; they are particularly abundant in the neighbourhood of the idiozome, but they are never seen within the latter. These are the thread-granules or mitochondria.[31] They often appear as granules in fixed preparations, and not rarely as rows of granules; but in life they are nearly always somewhat lengthened and usually rod-shaped or filamentous. The diameter of all the mitochondria in any one cell is commonly about the same, but the length varies considerably: it is quite usual for the length and breadth to be roughly proportional to those of a cigarette. The surface of mitochondria is everywhere smooth, the ends rounded. Mitochondria very seldom branch. It is often said that they have a capacity for independent movement, but it seems more likely that motion is sometimes imparted to them by the ground cytoplasm. We do not ordinarily see any objects in a cell that could be stages in their growth from small rudiments, and there is strong reason to believe that they usually multiply by transverse division.

A quarter of a century ago much was known about the arrangement of mitochondria in different kinds of cells, but very little about their significance for vital processes. The discovery that they could be separated in bulk by differential centrifuging of mashed tissue[33] made it possible to subject them to detailed chemical and enzymological analysis, and today we probably know more about their mode of action than about that of any other part of the cell, the chromosomes not excepted. We find in them the enzymes concerned with the degradation of pyruvic acid to carbon dioxide and water: that is to say, with the parts of the respiratory process known as the tricarboxylic acid cycle and the cytochrome system. It remains to relate their function to the complex internal structure revealed by the electron-microscope.

Small lipid globules (lipochondria) are distributed in the

cytoplasm, mostly in the vicinity of the idiozome (but never within it). Nearly all cells contain lipid globules in the cytoplasm, but they have been greatly overlooked, probably because they are not seen in routine paraffin sections. These globules may contain triglyceride, but usually consist mainly of more complex lipids, especially phospholipids and cerebrosides. Their refractive index is often low, and this suggests that they must contain water associated with their phospholipid content.[165] Sometimes a lipid cortex surrounds a non-lipid, probably aqueous core, but this structure is perhaps rarer than superficial appearances would suggest.[18]

The significance of lipid globules is obscure. Adipose fat accumulates mainly in particular cells set aside for the purpose, but nearly every cell contains globules of more complex lipids that are not used up when the animal is starved. The lipids of these globules are often highly unsaturated and therefore reduce osmium tetroxide and silver nitrate easily.

Certain cytoplasmic inclusions are built on such a small scale that the light-microscope cannot reveal their shape or structure. We are forced to rely on the electron-microscope. Since this instrument can only be applied to tissues that have been completely dried, it is not possible to examine these inclusions during the life of the cell. Fixed preparations must be used. A reaction occurs between what was present in life on one hand, and the fixative and other substances used in making the preparation on the other. What is studied under the electron-microscope is the reaction-product.[20] We lack the means of verification that are available with all objects that are large enough to be studied with the light-microscope during the life of the cell.

An electron-micrograph is generally regarded as 'good' if it shows much minute detail, or if the constituent parts appear in strong contrast with one another; but we have no means of knowing whether the details represent the relative positions of the parts in the living cell, nor do we know whether these parts were sharply separated from one another.

The only way in which we can learn to interpret electron-micrographs is by the study of known substances (especially proteins, lipoproteins, and lipids) that have been prepared for electron-microscopy in the same way as pieces of tissue. This kind of work is still in its infancy, but a most interesting start has been made with phospholipids.[156] These appear in electron-micrographs in the form of parallel membranes, often arranged concentrically. Similar membranes are often seen in electron-micrographs of cells.[60, 44] They are called 'Golgi apparatus' by many electron-microscopists. It seems better to regard them provisionally as phospholipids.[20, 22] These substances sometimes occur free in the cytoplasm of the living cell, but sometimes they are bound up in lipoprotein complexes. Certain fixatives and other reagents used in microtechnique 'unmask' the phospholipids of these complexes: that is to say, they set them free from combination with protein.[63] In an electron-micrograph there may be nothing to indicate in which form the phospholipid was present in the living cell.[20, 22] (See p. ix.)

Reaction-products of two kinds occur repeatedly in the cytoplasm of very diverse cells. They appear to represent two distinct objects, which may perhaps be of universal or almost universal occurrence. These are the endoplasmic reticulum and the 'small particles' of Palade (fig. 2).

The endoplasmic reticulum is a three-dimensional network

Fig. 2 (plate). A, *electron-micrograph representing part of the cytoplasm of a large phagocytic cell (macrophage) derived from the blood of the domestic fowl. The micrograph is very exceptional in representing not a section, but a whole mount of an extremely thin cell.*

f, *fold in cell membrane;* gc, *ground cytoplasm (in the strict sense);* l, *lipid droplet;* m, *mitochondrion (unusual in being branched);* r, *rounded component of the endoplasmic reticulum;* t, *trabecular component of the endoplasmic reticulum.*

B, *electron-micrograph representing a section of a small part of the basal region of an acinar cell from the pancreas of the rat.*

cm, *cell membrane;* er, *flattened components of the endoplasmic reticulum, seen in transverse section;* sp, *small particles of Palade.*

Reproduced from the Journal of Experimental Medicine[141] and the Journal of Biophysical and Biochemical Cytology,[140] by kind permission of the Editors of the journals and of Dr G. E. Palade and Dr K. R. Porter (authors of the papers in which the micrographs first appeared). The lettering on the micrographs has been altered.

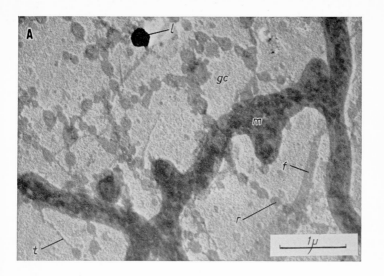

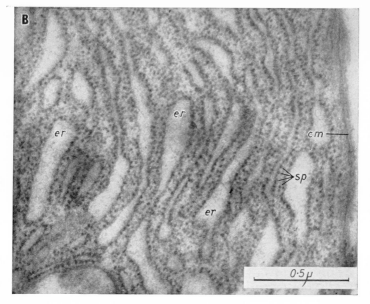

extending through most parts of the cytoplasm. It commonly consists of rounded components (fig. 2, A, *r*), joined by narrower elements that may be called trabeculae (*t*). The material forming the network is seen in sectional view to be dark externally and pale internally, and this has given rise to the opinion that the reticulum is hollow. If so, the rounded components are vesicles and the trabeculae are tubes, and all or nearly all the cavities are continuous. There is, however, no rigorous proof that this is so. It may be simply that the external layer has a greater affinity for osmium than the internal part: we do not know which is the denser.

The swollen components of the endoplasmic reticulum are not always rounded. Sometimes they are flattened and seem to resemble sacks piled one on another. In section the flattened 'sacks' appear as elongated spaces (fig. 2, B, *er*), though here again we have no proof that the objects are in fact hollow. They are connected with one another, like the rounded elements, by trabeculae, which again may or may not be tubular.

Although the flattened components of the endoplasmic reticulum are not individually recognizable under the light-microscope, yet large piles of them do sometimes reach microscopical dimensions. A well-known example is the striated material seen at the base of the exocrine cells of the pancreas. Striated cytoplasm of this kind was long ago named *ergastoplasme*,[38, 81] and the word is still used to denote this particular modification of the endoplasmic reticulum. The Nissl bodies of the neurones of vertebrates are similar in submicroscopic structure to the basal cytoplasm of the exocrine cell.[142]

There is not yet any sure knowledge of the significance for the life of the cell of the object that is represented by endoplasmic reticulum in electron-micrographs.

The name 'endoplasmic reticulum' is an unfortunate one. The object was first recognized in certain sarcoma cells, in which a very narrow, hyaline, marginal zone could be distinguished from the internal endoplasm. The reticulum was called endoplasmic because it was retricted to the inner zone.[151, 149] The differentiation of a special external zone or ectoplasm from a less hyaline endoplasm is found especially in free-living Protozoa and in certain other cells that are directly exposed to a non-cellular environment. It is far from being characteristic of cells in general. It is unusual in those that are bounded by other cells, and does not occur in spermatogonia. Yet it is thought likely that all cells contain a cytoplasmic inclusion that would appear in electron-micrographs as the 'endoplasmic' reticulum.

The 'small particles' associated particularly with the name of the American cytologist Palade[140] are far too minute to be seen separately by the light-microscope. There is strong reason to suppose that they contain a high proportion of RNA, in the form of ribonucleoprotein, and this acidic substance has an affinity for basic dyes (p. 90). Cytoplasm that is seen by light-microscopy to have a special affinity for these dyes can often be shown by electron-microscopy to possess small particles in particularly great abundance. In spermatogonia the small particles are few and the cytoplasm has little affinity for such dyes.

It is not possible to tell exactly where the small particles were in life, but in electron-micrographs many of them are usually situated on the outer side of the endoplasmic reticulum, which looks as though it has been peppered with them (fig. 2, B, *sp*). In some kinds of cells, however, the small particles are very numerous but separate from the reticulum. It is for this reason that these two cytoplasmic inclusions, so often associated, must be listed separately.

It is wise to regard with a certain amount of scepticism the information about cellular constituents provided by the electron-microscope. Nevertheless, one cannot fail to be struck by the regularity with which the endoplasmic reticulum and small particles appear in micrographs.

It remains to consider the ground cytoplasm. This term is used in two distinct senses. In light-microscopy it means the whole of the substance of the cell other than the visible inclusions. In this wide sense it thus *includes* the endoplasmic reticulum and small particles. When it is stated, for instance, that the refractive index of the ground cytoplasm is commonly about 1·353[163, 164] or that its pH is generally between 6·4 and 7·2, the figures given must be taken to represent a summation of the refractive index and pH of the substance, taken as a whole, that lies between the microscopically-visible inclusions. In the strict sense, however, the term 'ground cytoplasm' must apply only to the material in which the submicroscopical inclusions are embedded (fig. 2, A). In this sense, then, it excludes the endoplasmic reticulum and small particles. Even when the reticulum is bulky and the particles numerous, a large proportion of the cell is occupied by the ground cytoplasm in the strict sense. It is regrettable that we should know so little of this cellular component. In electronmicrographs that are considered 'good', the space in question is often criss-crossed by very fine fibres. These are thought to be formed of protein. We can scarcely be far wrong in supposing that the ground cytoplasm in the strict sense consists mainly of water and protein, associated with one another through the hydrophil groups of the protein (p. 20). The latter may be supposed to exist partly as long, extended polypeptide chains (p. 19), linked to one another here and there to form a weak gel, partly as globules consisting of such chains wound up into skeins.[80] The water must hold some of the cytoplasmic ions in solution (principally potassium and phosphate, with some magnesium and bicarbonate, and other ions in lesser amount).

Since this book is concerned mainly with light-microscopy, the expression 'ground cytoplasm' is to be understood in the wide sense, except where the contrary is distinctly indicated.

CHAPTER 2

Introduction to Fixation

There is only one really reliable criterion by which we can determine whether the image that we see with the microscope is a good representation of what existed in life, and that criterion is comparison with the living cell. We have nowadays several excellent ways of overcoming the natural transparency of this object. Phase-contrast and interference microscopy are the chief methods, and vital dyeing, though at the moment partially eclipsed, remains potentially as illuminating as ever. Since we possess these reliable means of obtaining knowledge, it may reasonably be asked why we need also the elaborate procedures that form the subject-matter of this book.

Many kinds of cells cannot be isolated for separate study while still alive. Such cells can only be examined in permanent preparations. It is a great advantage to be able to cut tissues and cells into thin slices. The relations of the cells to one another and to the intercellular matter are much better shown in this way than when cells are teased apart for direct study while still alive. The living cell of many-celled organisms cannot be sectioned effectively. Even if a slice could be cut, it would not remain alive nor retain its form. Tissues and cells need to be stabilized in structure and held firmly while being sliced. In fact, they require to be 'fixed' more or less in their living form and then embedded in some solid material before they can be sectioned. When the process of fixation has been carried out, nearly all their parts can be dyed in contrasting colours, and this makes observation much easier. Vital dyeing, invaluable though it is, is applicable only to particular components of the cell. Again, few histochemical tests are applicable to unfixed tissues. Beyond all this, it is a convenience to be able to store away permanent preparations, ready for instant examination at any time.

For these reasons it is usual to fix a piece of tissue in a fluid called a fixative; to embed it after fixation in some solid medium, such as paraffin wax, that will hold its constituent parts in the right relation to one another during sectioning; then to section it; next to dye the sections, often in two or more contrasting colours; and finally to mount the dyed sections in a medium that renders them transparent.

In this book we are concerned with the principles underlying fixation, embedding, dyeing, and mounting. We are not immediately concerned with the application of histochemical tests, a subject to which another volume in this series of Biological Monographs is devoted.[53] Nevertheless, the present work is largely chemical in outlook, and the preparation of tissues for study follows the same general routine whether a histochemical test is to be applied or not. It is therefore hoped that the book may be useful to those whose main interests are in histochemical or cytochemical analysis. We shall study *what happens* when we fix, embed, dye, and mount tissues (and especially the cells that they contain).

If a piece of tissue is cut out of a living or recently dead organism and no special care is taken to keep it alive or maintain its structure, it will soon undergo marked changes. If left in the air, it will lose water by evaporation and shrink; if left in a fluid, it is likely to undergo osmotic swelling or shrinkage. If these distortions are prevented, it will still be subject to attack by bacteria and moulds. Even if these are excluded by asepsis, the tissue will gradually fall to pieces by self-digestion or 'autolysis'.[74] Cells contain enzymes, collectively known as 'cathepsin', capable of dissolving their own protein constituents when they die. These enzymes (two proteinases, a carboxypeptidase, and an amino-peptidase) show a remarkable resemblance to those of the digestive tract. In life their function is presumably synthetic.

To preserve a piece of tissue one requires a fluid that will not shrink or swell or dissolve or distort; will kill bacteria and moulds; and will render the autolytic enzymes inactive. Such a fluid is a *preservative*. A *fixative* must do everything that a preservative does, but in addition it must modify the tissues in such a way that they become capable of *resisting* subsequent treatments of various kinds. Of these treatments the ones that are most likely to cause damage are embedding, sectioning, and mounting (though the latter is not damaging if the tissue has already been severely shrunken while being embedded). Apart from the partial protection it gives against damage from these processes, fixation usually makes many tissue-constituents (especially chromatin) readily colourable by suitable dyes.

Not every tissue-constituent requires fixation, and some are not capable of being fixed. Chitin, cellulose, starch-grains, scleroproteins, amorphous silica, and certain inorganic crystals are examples of hard, stable substances, scarcely or not at all subject to distortion or decay. Other substances, such as the soluble sugars, cannot be retained in their natural sites in the tissues by any fixative. Glycogen is the only soluble carbohydrate that is at all frequently retained in finished microscopical preparations.

Though usually soft or indeed liquid, triglycerides do not require fixation if lipid-solvents are avoided in subsequent treatment. Some fixatives have no effect on lipids, but this does not by any means make them useless, for neither the cell nor intercellular material is held together by lipids. If, however, the common proteins are not stabilized, tissues and cells fall to pieces. The essential function of fixation is the stabilization of the protein framework of the cell.

Fixation can be achieved by heat, but this method is seldom used except for blood-films. It tends to cause distortion, but presents the advantage that nothing is dissolved out of the cell.

Most fixatives are solids used in aqueous solution, but some are organic liquids that can be used without dilution. The number of chemical compounds that are useful as fixatives is very small. The seven unmixed or 'primary' fixatives chosen for mention in this book are listed below. All fixatives fall easily into two groups, according to their obvious reactions with soluble proteins. Some of them, when mixed with a solution of albumin, produce a coagulum: others do not. The ones that produce a coagulum in a test-tube transform homogeneous protoplasm into a microscopical spongework.

Against each fixative in the list below is marked its 'standard concentration'. This is the concentration at or near which it is commonly used in fixation. Throughout the book, except where the contrary is distinctly stated, it is to be understood that when reference is made to one of the seven selected primary fixatives, it was used at the concentration shown in the list (or at a concentration so close to this that no difference in result could be anticipated).

COAGULANTS

Ethanol (ethyl alcohol). C_2H_5OH. A light, colourless fluid, miscible with water in all proportions. Standard concentration, undiluted (absolute).

Mercuric chloride. $HgCl_2$. Colourless crystals, soluble in water at about 7%. Standard concentration, saturated aqueous solution.

Chromium trioxide. CrO_3. Brownish-red crystals, giving a strongly acid solution in water, in which it is extremely soluble. Standard concentration, 0·5% aqueous.

NON-COAGULANTS

Formaldehyde. H_2CO. Colourless gas, very soluble in water. Standard concentration, 4% aqueous.

Osmium tetroxide. OsO_4. Pale yellow crystals, soluble in water at about 7%. Standard concentration, 1% aqueous.

Potassium dichromate. $K_2Cr_2O_7$. Orange-red crystals, giving a weakly acid solution in water, in which it is soluble at about 10%. Standard concentration, 1·5% aqueous.

Acetic acid. $H_3C.COOH$. Colourless liquid, miscible with water in all proportions. Standard concentration, 5%.

Since each of the primary fixatives has its virtues and defects,

C

it is usual in practice to mix two or more of them together. Fixative mixtures will be considered in chapter 5 (p. 59). Their effects on tissues can only be understood when those of their components are known. Further, the proportions of the primary fixatives in the mixtures have been very arbitrarily chosen. For these reasons, any scientific account of fixation must start with the primary fixatives and be concerned mainly with these.

Small pieces of tissue are best fixed by direct immersion, since this brings the fixative most rapidly into contact with the cells throughout the piece. When it is necessary to fix a piece of tissue a centimetre or more thick, it is best to inject the fixative through a blood-vessel in order to send it quickly to all depths. This method of 'perfusion' has the disadvantage that the total amount of fixative that can be contained in the blood-vessels is usually small, and nothing outside the vessels is fixed until the fixative substance has passed through their walls into the intercellular spaces and thus reached the cells.

The purpose of fixation is usually to stabilize the tissues so that they retain as nearly as possible the form they had in life, but clearly it is not the purpose to leave their chemical composition unchanged. This would indeed be the negation of fixation, for the cells would be still alive or like recently dead ones. The purpose is to change the chemical composition in such a way as to confer structural stability. This fact by no means makes histochemical studies impossible, for certain tissue-constituents may be left unaltered, and others only altered in part.

The structural formula for amino-acids in general is conveniently written in the way shown here, because such formulae may easily be joined together to make a protein chain. The letter R in the formula represents any of the radicles that distinguish the various amino-acids from one another. In forming a protein, the amino-acids condense together with elimination of one

$$\text{molecule of water at each peptide link} \left(\begin{array}{c} O \\ \parallel \quad H \\ -C\!-\!N- \end{array} \right).$$

In the formula representing part of a protein chain, certain conventions have been adopted. The radicles characteristic of

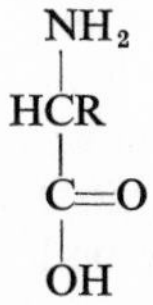

$$NH$$
$$HC(CH_2)_4NH_2 \quad \textit{lysine}$$
$$C{=}O$$
$$NH$$
$$HC.CH_2\langle\bigcirc\rangle OH \quad \textit{tyrosine}$$
$$C{=}O$$
$$NH$$
$$HC(CH_2)_2C\diagup^{O}_{OH} \quad \textit{glutamic acid}$$
$$C{=}O$$

$$NH_2$$
$$HCR$$
$$C{=}O$$
$$OH$$

*General formula for
amino-acids*

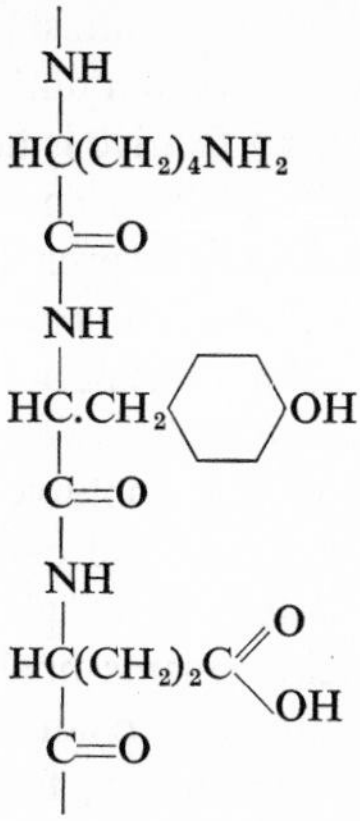

*Three amino-acids as part
of a protein chain*

each amino-acid are written on the right of the formula in each case, although in fact they project in different directions; and the repeated part or backbone of the formula is shown as straight, though in nature it is folded, either to form a simple zigzag or in more complex ways. These conventions will be found to simplify the explanation of the reactions of proteins with fixatives and dyes.

The first requirement of a fixative is that it should not be proteolytic. Any substance that breaks the peptide links and sets free soluble amino-acids is the opposite of a fixative. The changes produced by a fixative must tend in the other direction, towards stability.

One may broadly distinguish two kinds of fixation of protein, additive and non-additive. In the former, certain atoms of the fixative combine chemically with some part of the protein and remain in combination. In the latter, no such obvious addition of atoms occurs. Ethanol is a non-additive fixative in the sense that none of its constituent atoms joins itself to protein, so far as is known. The 'nature' of the protein is, however, profoundly changed by its action, and the substance is therefore said to be

'denatured'.[5, 6, 136, 154] The most obvious change is loss of solubility with resultant coagulation.

When a denaturing fixative is added to a solution of albumin,
coagulation usually follows so quickly that it appears to be
instantaneous. In fact, however, denaturation can be shown to
proceed by stages. The first effect is an increase in reactivity;
there then follows a flocculation or aggregation into minute
particles, which are soluble in weak acids and alkalis; finally the
flocculi join into a clot, soluble only by reagents that cause
proteolysis. Flocculation and clot-formation are both included
in the term coagulation. Throughout all these changes the backbone of the protein remains unaltered. Some authors mean by
denaturation almost any change in a protein that increases
reactivity but does not destroy the backbone.[136] In this book the
term will be used in a more limited sense to indicate a marked
change involving the relation of the protein with the surrounding
water. This change results in coagulation.

The chief hydrophil groups of proteins are the $-NH_2$ and

$-C\overset{\displaystyle O}{\underset{\displaystyle OH}{\diagup}}$ groups of basic and acidic amino-acids, the $-OH$ group

of tyrosine, and the $\overset{|}{\underset{|}{C}}\!=\!O$ groups of the backbone. Whether a

particular protein be dispersed as a sol or held together by cross-
links to form a gel, it will ordinarily be related to water molecules
by such groups as these. When a protein is denatured, the relations with water are somehow disturbed. It may be supposed that
ethanol, a dehydrating agent, competes with the protein for the
water, and that the active groups, now no longer associated with
water, are more free to make fresh bonds with one another. The
formation of fresh bonds, so close as to exclude much of the
water that formerly lay between protein chains, would cause
coagulation. Interfaces between 'dry' protein and the surrounding fluid would thus be formed; and since these would scatter
light, the transparent sol or gel would change into a white
coagulum.

Various reactive groups that were present in the unaltered

protein in a latent condition are unmasked by denaturing and now respond to tests for their presence. This applies to various ionizing side-chains of the constituent amino-acids, especially the –SH of cysteine, the –S—S– of cystine, the phenyl of tyrosine, and the indolyl of tryptophane. The cause of this increase in reactivity is not known, but it may be a straightening of much-folded backbones and consequent exposure of previously-hidden side-groups. The protein is now more accessible both to dyes and to digestive enzymes. The specificity of the original protein is at the same time generally lost. This is most evident if the protein is or forms part of an enzyme.

Proteins can be denatured by very diverse means. Heat alone is effective, if water be present; in the complete absence of moisture, however, even a temperature of 100° C does not suffice to denature. Exposure to ultraviolet light or ultrasonic waves, subjection to very high pressure, and extension in extremely thin films can cause the denaturing of proteins, but these methods are not ordinarily used in microtechnique.

In additive fixation a part or the whole of the fixative molecule adds itself to the substance that it fixes, by making ionic or covalent links. In the fixation of proteins, the link is usually with the side-groups of one or more particular amino-acids. Additive fixation is sometimes coagulant, sometimes not.

An additive fixative need not necessarily alter the reactions of a protein very profoundly. For instance, it might act only on tyrosine side-groups, and if these were sparsely represented in a particular protein, most of the amino-acids might be able to retain their character and show their usual responses to reagents. The rest of the protein might undergo changes similar to those that occur in non-additive fixation. Thus there need not be a very sharp distinction between the two kinds of fixation, so far as the protein as a whole is concerned. Nevertheless, it is convenient to restrict the term 'denaturing' to cases in which the protein does not undergo chemical combination.

Different primary fixatives penetrate into tissues at different rates. Other things being equal, it is desirable that a fixative should penetrate quickly, so that the tissue may be stabilized in structure before autolysis has damaged it. In designing fixative mixtures it is helpful to know the relative rates of penetration of the components, for ideally one component should not outstrip another.

To study the rate of penetration of fixatives, it is best to begin by using a homogeneous protein gel in place of a piece of tissue.[120, 21] A suitable gel may be made by dissolving gelatine at 15% in warm white-of-egg.[21] This material may be used as a crude model of cytoplasm, for its refractive index (and hence its protein-content) is about the same. While still warm it can be drawn into glass tubes, and the gel then allowed to set. If one end of the tube is inserted into a solution of a coagulant fixative, the rate of penetration can easily be noted, since the material becomes white and opaque on coagulation. To find how far a non-coagulant fixative has penetrated, it is only necessary to turn the tube upside down in a bowl of warm water, for the unfixed gel then runs out, while the fixed material remains in the tube.[21] It will be understood that what is measured in these experiments is the distance through which the substance under test has moved at the concentration that is just sufficient to fix the gel.

Fixatives penetrate into the gel rapidly at first and progressively more slowly as time goes on. It has been shown that nearly all fixatives move forward in accordance with the laws of diffusion.[120] If d is the distance penetrated in time t, and K is a constant depending on the fixative used, then

$$d = K\sqrt{t}.$$

Distance may be measured in mm and time in hours. K then represents the distance in mm through which the fixative has moved forward in one hour, at a concentration sufficient to fix the protein.

It is convenient to transform the equation just given into its logarithmic form,

$$\log d = \log K + \tfrac{1}{2}\log t.$$

This, when graphed, will necessarily give a straight line. If a set of figures for d and t, obtained in an experiment, are converted into logarithms and marked on a graph, it will at once be seen whether they lie approximately on a straight line. This is so with nearly all fixatives. (See, for example, fig. 3.)

Where the straight line crosses the ordinate line, log t has

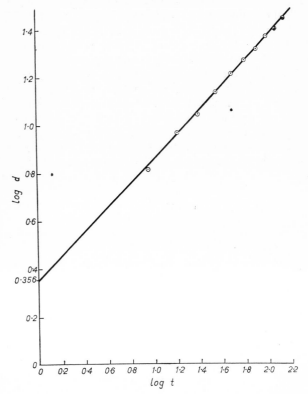

Fig. 3. *Graph showing the rate of penetration of mercuric chloride (at standard concentration) into gelatine-albumin gel.* t *is time in hours;* d *is the distance penetrated in mm.*[21, 24]

become zero and log d = log K. One can therefore read off the value of log K on the ordinate line, and the antilogarithm of the figure obtained is therefore K. In the case of mercuric chloride penetrating into gelatine-albumin gel, the K-value is 2·27. Form-aldehyde shows the highest K-value (3·6) among the seven selected primary fixatives. Chromium trioxide is slow ($K = 1·12$).

It is convenient to make the units of the abscissa-scale (log t) one-half of those of the ordinate-scale (log d). Then, if the fraction before log t in the logarithmic equation is $\frac{1}{2}$ (that is, if d is proportional to the square root of t), the slope of the line will be 45°. This is so with most fixatives (see fig. 3).

Few tissues are sufficiently homogeneous to give clear-cut results in tests of rate of penetration. Liver, however, is suitable, and certain coagulant fixatives leave a clear indication of how far they have moved into this organ, since the fixed tissue is whitish and opaque. Experiments with mercuric chloride show that here also the laws of diffusion are obeyed. The K-value of mercuric chloride diffusing into liver is 0·84. So far as is known, all fixatives penetrate much more slowly into liver than into gelatine-albumin gel, perhaps because they are held back by the lipids of cell-membranes and ground cytoplasm. There is, however, a general agreement in the results obtained with gels and liver. Thus chromium trioxide penetrates much more slowly than mercuric chloride into both.

It is important to realize how rapidly the rate of penetration of fixatives falls off with time. With a K-value of 0·84, mercuric chloride penetrates into liver a distance of 20μ (the diameter of a large cell) in just over two seconds. That is to say, it penetrates this small distance at the rate of 36 mm an hour; but actually it only penetrates 0·84 mm in one hour, and it would take 77 days to penetrate 36 mm. These facts emphasize the importance of using small pieces of tissue for fixation. Pieces several cm thick are only adequately fixed in their external parts, unless they are perfused with the fixative.

Instructions are often given as to the time during which a particular fixative should act, but it is usually safe to disregard these. For light-microscopy it is convenient as a general rule to fix overnight (say 18 hours). Little difference will in many cases be noticed if the period is extended to several days, or even weeks or years. A shorter time than 18 hours suffices for the pieces used in cytology, which are seldom more than 3 mm thick, but over-night fixation is not harmful. In electron-microscopy osmium tetroxide is the most usual fixative. There is some evidence that proteins may eventually be dissolved by this fixative, after having been well fixed at first. Pieces about 1 mm thick are used, and it is quite usual to fix only for an hour or two, or even for less than an hour.

The structure exhibited in a fixed microscopical preparation is almost always to some extent artificial, for no fixative is perfect. Artifacts are of two kinds, extrinsic and intrinsic.

Extrinsic artifacts are those formed of material brought in by the fixative and deposited in the tissues. One may take as an example the black granules often seen in material fixed in mer-curic chloride solution (p. 36). Artifacts of this kind can usually be avoided. They are commonly caused by the reaction of the fixative left in the tissues with fluids in which the tissues are subsequently immersed. An extrinsic artifact, once formed, may often be removed by the use of special solvents.

The intrinsic artifacts are the distorted structures of the tissue-constituents themselves. Very great changes are undergone by a cell when it is fixed by a coagulant fixative, embedded in paraffin, sectioned, dyed, and mounted; and fixation itself is the chief cause of these changes. What happens may be studied by comparing fig. 4 with fig. 1 (p. 4). The cell is irregularly shrunken, and the ground cytoplasm is transformed into a coagulum consisting of a spongework of protein strands. No part of the original substance of the cell is left in the meshes of the network, which are filled only with the mounting medium. The size of the meshes depends on the particular fixative used. They are often even larger than those shown in the diagram (fig. 4). The coarseness of the coagulum is not always realized, because the strands cross one another at different depths in the thickness of an ordinary section, so as not to leave any very obvious gaps, and rather feeble dyes are generally used for this part of the cell; but if a crudely coagulant fixative is used, and very thin sections are strongly dyed with iron haematein (p. 121), the gaps become obvious.

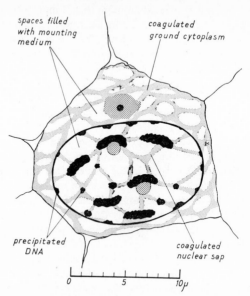

spaces filled
with mounting
medium

coagulated
ground cytoplasm

precipitated
DNA

coagulated
nuclear sap

0   5   10μ

Fig. 4. A typical spermatogonium, as seen in a routine micro-
scopical preparation (diagrammatic). The cell has been fixed in
a coagulant fixative, embedded in paraffin, dyed, and mounted.
Compare with fig. 1 (p. 4).

No traces of the mitochondria or lipid droplets remain. The
centriole, if present, is intact; the idiozome sometimes but not
always persists. The nuclear sap has been coagulated, like the
ground cytoplasm. The heterochromatic segments of the chromosomes are still visible and strongly dyed, but the rest of the
DNA has been thrown down in the form of an irregular precipitate scattered here and there on the strands of the coagulum
and on the inside of the nuclear membrane. The nucleoli retain
their form but are somewhat shrunken.

The non-coagulant fixatives, especially osmium tetroxide and
formaldehyde, cause much less initial change in structure than
the coagulants. Indeed, while the cells still lie in these fixatives

they often look remarkably lifelike. Embedding in paraffin, however, usually causes serious distortion.

Ideally a fixative would leave the volume of a piece of tissue

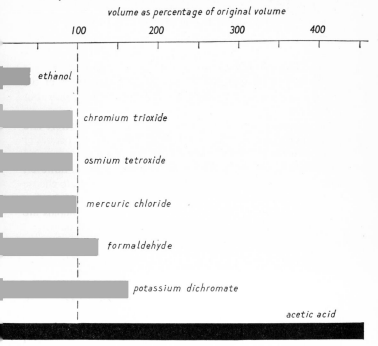

volume as percentage of original volume

	100	200	300	400

ethanol

chromium trioxide

osmium tetroxide

mercuric chloride

formaldehyde

potassium dichromate

acetic acid

Fig. 5. Diagram showing the changes in volume undergone by gelatine-albumin gel when acted upon for 18 hours by the selected primary fixatives. The latter were used at their standard concentrations.[21]

and of its constituent cells unaltered, and resistant to alteration by fluids in which it was subsequently placed. Many fixatives shrink tissues; some leave them scarcely changed in volume, while others swell them, but in any case the tissue is liable to subsequent shrinkage.

The results of shrinkage and swelling lend themselves more

readily to quantitative analysis than do the other intrinsic artifacts caused by fixatives. Interesting experiments can be made
with the same gelatine-albumin gel as is used in studies of rate of
penetration. The results are shown in fig. 5. Acetic acid swells
strongly, and indeed this is one of the main reasons why it is
included in so many fixative mixtures, for the swelling counteracts the shrinkage caused subsequently by embedding, especially if the swollen cells are fixed in their swollen state by a
coagulant fixative (see p. 62). Fig. 5 shows that most of the
primary fixatives do not alter the volume of the gel greatly, but
ethanol shrinks it strongly.

Whole animals or whole organs may be measured before and
after fixation, and at various stages in the subsequent processes of
microtechnique; or cubes may be cut out of large organs and
treated in the same way. The most interesting results, however,
are those obtained by the study of single cells. It is best to choose
loose, spherical cells for this purpose, since they are simplest
from the geometrical point of view. The eggs of echinoids are
suitable in this respect. Some results are shown in Table 1.

TABLE 1

The volumes of unfertilized eggs of the echinoid, Arbacia pustulosa, *at
various stages of preparation for microscopical study, expressed as
percentages of the volumes while alive in sea-water. Each figure is
calculated from the mean diameter of 10 to 15 eggs. (Data of Hertwig*[99])

Fixative	Volume in			
	fixative, 24 hours	ethanol, 70%	ethanol, abs.	xylene
formaldehyde (in sea-water)	105	70	50	48
ethanol	48	—	—	41

Comparable results are shown by studies of the spermatocytes
of the common snail, *Helix aspersa.*[161] When they have been
fixed in formaldehyde solution, embedded in paraffin, sectioned,

and mounted in Canada balsam, their volume is only 34% of what it was when they were alive; yet formaldehyde is superior to the six other primary fixatives in this respect. Ethanol is the worst of all: the final volume is only 19% of the original.

The addition of 'indifferent' or non-fixative salts to fixatives often improves the results obtained. A saline solution may be prepared, having about the same osmotic pressure as the body-fluids of the organism from which tissue is to be taken, and the fixative substance dissolved in this instead of distilled water. It follows that the complete solution is hypertonic. This would be thought likely to cause great shrinkage of the cells, but in fact shrinkage is reduced by the presence of the indifferent salt, and indeed that is precisely why it is used. The way in which it acts is obscure.[21] The use of an indifferent salt is particularly helpful when the fixative is chromium trioxide or formaldehyde.

To make a general study of the artifacts caused by fixation, separate cells are often examined in a suitable saline solution while still alive, and a fixative is then allowed to run under the coverslip. The immediate effects are thus easily observed. The classical work of this kind was done by dark-ground microscopy.[177] The introduction of phase-contrast microscopy resulted in a renewal of interest in work of this kind.[47, 66, 147] The method is valuable but open to two objections. First, it is clearly a test of preservation, not of fixation. Secondly, it shows only how fixatives affect cells that come into immediate contact with them. Many valuable fixatives damage the most superficial cells of a piece of tissue but give good results at a little depth below the surface. When separate cells are examined, they all react like superficial cells, and the fixative may be wrongly condemned.

To overcome these objections, small pieces of suitable tissue may be fixed, embedded, sectioned, dyed, and mounted, and the resulting preparation carefully compared with what can be seen in living cells from the same material. It is best to choose tissues that are readily available but difficult to fix well. The testes of various animals (mammals, urodeles, insects) are suitable.[30, 21] Embedding in paraffin is particularly likely to cause distortion, and this medium should therefore be chosen for a rigorous test.

The finished slides of the same material fixed in different ways should be carefully compared by an observer who does not know which is which. There are strong prejudices in favour of particular fixatives, and few cytologists would be able to judge the slides impartially if they knew which fixative had been used in the preparation of each.

The difficulty of judging electron-micrographs objectively has already been mentioned (p. 9).

CHAPTER 3

Coagulant Primary Fixatives

In this chapter and the next each of the selected primary fixatives (p. 17) will be considered separately. Its properties will be summarized in a systematic way. The intention is to give as complete a summary of the fixative action of each substance as is possible in the present state of knowledge. The information will include a good deal that has been scattered through chapter 2.

Since the present chapter and the next are likely to be used for reference by some who have not read the earlier part of the book, it is necessary to explain once more what is meant by 'standard concentration'. This is a fixed concentration, approximately that at which the substance in question is commonly used in fixation. Throughout this book, except where the contrary is stated, every remark about the action of a primary fixative refers to its action at (or very near) its standard concentration.

The expressions w/v, w/w, &c. are defined on p. xv.

The oxidation-potentials (o.p.) quoted in chapters 3 and 4 are taken from Casselman.[52, 54] The K-values given in these chapters refer to the rate of penetration into gelatine-albumin gel (p. 22), or, in the case of acetic acid, into gelatine-nucleoprotein gel.

Fixatives that stabilize the proteins of the cell quite well may leave much to be desired where cell-aggregates are concerned, for these may be distorted during fixation or embedding, in such a way as to leave artificial spaces. Groups of cells may become separated from other groups or from basement membranes or connective tissue. Although this book is primarily concerned with cytology, yet the needs of the histologist and microscopical anatomist must be kept in mind, and the effects of the selected primary fixatives on cell-aggregates will therefore be briefly noted.

The properties of the selected fixatives are summarized on the pages listed here:

When added at the proper concentration to a solution of albumin, coagulant fixatives separate the protein from the water as a curd or coagulum (p. 20). This reaction serves to define them. They transform the proteins of the cytoplasm (and often the nuclear sap as well) into a sponge-work. This does not necessarily destroy structure at the microscopical level, since the meshes of the spongework may be very fine; but non-coagulant fixatives are nearly always used in electron-microscopy. The production of a spongework is helpful to the penetration of embedding media, especially paraffin. The coagulant fixatives are much less diverse in their action on cells than the non-coagulants are.

ETHANOL (ethyl alcohol)

Standard concentration. Undiluted (absolute).

Formula. C_2H_5OH.

Description. A light, colourless fluid, miscible with water in all proportions.

Ionization. Not ionized.

Oxidation-potential. Low (95% ethanol, 0·45 volt).

Reactions with proteins. A non-additive or denaturing coagulant of many proteins. It does not coagulate zein, gliadin, or nucleoprotein. Ethanol is a powerful 'unmasking' agent for lipids; that is to say, it sets them free from combination with protein. It acts in this way when used as a fixative[61] and also when used after the tissue has been fixed by a substance that does not itself unmask.[63]

Reactions with nucleic acids. Precipitates but does not fix them.

Reactions with lipids. These are not chemically changed by ethanol, which tends rather to dissolve them than to fix them. This tendency, however, is weaker than is commonly supposed. Tripalmitin and tristearin are insoluble in cold ethanol, and so are several other common lipids of the tissues. Triolein, lecithin, and oleic acid are soluble; other fatty acids and cholesterol slightly so.

Reactions with carbohydrates. Precipitates glycogen without fixing it.

Rate of penetration. Moderate.

Shrinkage or swelling. Shrinks excessively.

Hardening. Hardens excessively.

Method of washing out. Since ethanol is miscible in all proportions with the antemedia (p. 73) used in embedding (and also with water), and since it has no tendency to form an extrinsic artifact, no special washing out is necessary.

Effect on the appearance of cells in microscopical preparations. It produces a coarse coagulum in cytoplasm and nucleus, and destroys mitochondria. Lipid droplets tend to fuse and may dissolve.

In paraffin sections, cell aggregates are shrunken apart from one another; cytoplasm is often piled up against the cell-membrane on the side opposite to that from which the fixative penetrated. Lipid droplets are not present; chromosomes are not distinctly seen.

Most fixatives render tissues more basic or more acidic than they were in the unfixed state, because they react with and block the acidic or basic side-groups of certain amino-acids. As a result, the affinity of the protein for basic and acid dyes is changed (p. 90). Ethanol is exceptional in this respect. Since it does not attack any of the side-groups, it leaves proteins neither more basic nor more acidic than they were before fixation, and dyes may therefore be used to find whether basic or acidic side-groups predominated in the living tissues. Nucleoprotein remains strongly colourable by basic dyes, but it is not stabilized in position in the

D

cell, and may even eventually be dissolved out. Ethanol is therefore a very poor fixative for nuclei as well as for chromosomes.

Compatibility with other fixatives. Compatible with mercuric chloride, formaldehyde, and acetic acid. Since it tends to be oxidized through aldehyde to acetic acid, it should not ordinarily be mixed with chromium trioxide, potassium dichromate, or osmium tetroxide (though its reaction with the two latter is slow).

MERCURIC CHLORIDE

Standard concentration. Saturated aqueous solution.

Formula. $HgCl_2$.

Description. Colourless, needle-shaped crystals. A covalent compound, with much lower melting-point than most salts: sublimes easily. Soluble in water at about 7%; readily soluble in ethanol and in benzene. Very poisonous.

Ionization. Ionizes only partially, with hydrolysis, to give $[HgCl_4]^=$ (particularly abundant in the presence of other chlorides), Hg^{++}, hydronium ions (the pH of the standard solution is about 3·2), and other ions.

Oxidation-potential. Rather a strong oxidizer (o.p. about 0·75 volt).

Reactions with proteins. An additive, coagulant fixative. The reactions depend on the pH at which the fixative is used.[88a]

If the pH is well below (more acid than) the iso-electric point of the protein, the $-NH_2$ groups of the basic amino-acids will mostly be ionized as $-\overset{+}{N}H_3$. There will therefore be electrostatic

$$\begin{array}{c} | \\ NH \\ | \\ HC(CH_2)_4\overset{+}{N}H_3 \\ | \\ C{=}O \\ | \end{array}$$

Lysine forming part of a protein chain, in a solution on the acid side of the iso-electric point

attraction between this positively charged group and the negatively charged ion, $[HgCl_4]^=$, which could associate itself with such groups in two previously separate protein chains and thus hold them together. The mercury thus adds itself to the protein in the form of an ion. The reaction is promoted by the presence of sodium chloride, since added chlorides increase the amount of the reactive ion.

In the neighbourhood of the iso-electric point, the $-NH_2$ groups

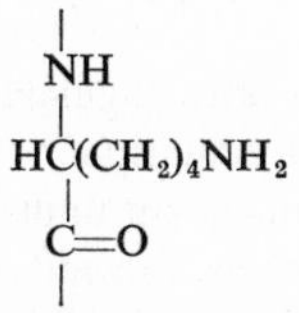

$$
\begin{array}{c}
| \\
NH \\
| \\
HC(CH_2)_4NH_2 \\
| \\
C{=}O \\
|
\end{array}
$$

Lysine forming part of a protein chain, in a solution at or near the iso-electric point

of the basic amino-acids are not ionized. It is now the undissociated salt, $HgCl_2$, that reacts. Mercury can accept extra electrons from electron-donor atoms, such as nitrogen. The compound formed resembles the 'ammine' formed by the combination of ammonia with mercuric chloride.[173] The lysine/mercuric chloride

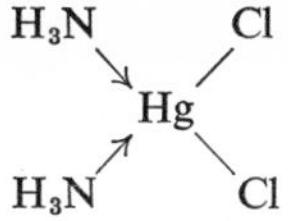

$$
\begin{array}{ccc}
H_3N & & Cl \\
& \searrow \quad \swarrow & \\
& Hg & \\
& \nearrow \quad \searrow & \\
H_3N & & Cl
\end{array}
$$

The compound of ammonia with mercuric chloride

bond formed in this way is a very loose one. The reaction is opposed by sodium chloride, and the coagulum produced may indeed be dissolved (and fixation thus undone) by addition of this salt.

In alkaline solutions the mercuric ion, Hg^{++}, reacts with the $-COOH$ groups of acidic proteins; but fixatives are rarely alkaline.

Mercuric chloride can also react with the cysteine groups of proteins, forming a bridge that connects these groups in previously separate protein chains.

|
NH
|
HC.CH₂.SH
|
C=O
|

*Cysteine as part of
a protein chain*

|
NH
|
HC.CH₂.S—Hg—S—H₂C.CH
|
C=O
|

|
NH
|
CH
|
C=O
|

*Mercury forming a link between cysteine
side-groups in two protein chains*

Mercuric chloride does not coagulate nucleoprotein solutions very powerfully: there is flocculation, not formation of a coherent clot. It acts on lipoproteins as an unmasking agent.[61]

Reactions with nucleic acids. Precipitates weakly.[76, 146]

Reactions with lipids. Mercuric chloride leaves triglycerides untouched. It forms compounds with phospholipids, but their solubilities in lipid-solvents do not appear to have been studied.

Reactions with carbohydrates. None is described.

Rate of penetration. Moderate ($K = 2 \cdot 2$). (See fig. 3, p. 23.)

Shrinkage or swelling. Shrinks gelatine-albumin gel and whole livers slightly.

Hardening. Hardens moderately.

Method of washing out. Mercuric chloride leaves black particles, generally a few μ in diameter, in the tissues. These are said to consist of metallic mercury.[119] They can be removed by iodine in alcoholic solution, presumably by formation of mercuric iodide. Iodine colours the tissues, but it may be removed by soaking in 70% ethanol or (much more quickly) by the action of sodium thiosulphate.

$$2[S_2O_3]^= \quad + \quad I_2 \quad \rightarrow \quad [S_4O_6]^= \quad + \quad 2I^-$$
Thiosulphate   *Tetra-thionate*   *Iodide*

Effect on the appearance of cells in microscopical preparations. While the cell still lies in the fixative, it is better preserved than by any other coagulant fixative. Its shape is well maintained, the ground cytoplasm and nuclear sap are finely coagulated, and mitochondria are not destroyed.

In paraffin sections the cytoplasm is rather badly shrunken and the cells tend to separate from one another; chromosomes are not well fixed; mitochondria and lipid droplets are usually not present.

Proteins are more readily coloured by basic dyes than they are after the action of any other fixative. The –COOH side-groups of their acidic amino-acids are presumably intact in the usual circumstances of fixation. The special affinity for basic dyes must be attributed in part to the coagulation of protein chains in a form that permits the dye ions to penetrate easily between them to reach their sites of action. There is some affinity for acid dyes, and it is therefore clear that the amino-groups of the proteins are not completely blocked.

Compatibility with other fixatives. Compatible with any of the selected primary fixatives.

CHROMIUM TRIOXIDE

Standard concentration. 0·5% w/v aqueous solution.

Formula. CrO_3.

Description. Brownish-red deliquescent crystals, extremely soluble in water (a saturated solution is about 62% w/W).

Ionization. In water it forms chromic acid, H_2CrO_4, which cannot be isolated. A small amount of this remains undissociated in water, while the greater part of it ionizes as dichromate, $[Cr_2O_7]^=$, and the rest mostly as hydrogen chromate, $[HCrO_4]^-$, with sufficient hydronium ions to give a 1% solution a pH of 1·2.[51, 52]

Oxidation-potential. This is much the strongest oxidizer of all fixatives (o.p. about 1·1 volt), the dichromate ion being readily reduced to the chromic ion, Cr^{+++}, or to chromic oxide, Cr_2O_3.

Reactions with proteins. A powerful coagulant of albumin and many other proteins, including nucleoprotein. Chromium trioxide does not fix gelatine gels. It is probably an additive fixative, but the reactions involved are not known. The affinity of proteins for basic dyes is rather low after fixation by chromium trioxide, and this suggests blocking of the –COOH groups of the acidic amino-acids. It has been suggested, however, that acidic proteins are not fixed but simply dissolve away.[169]

Reactions with nucleic acids. DNA is precipitated from solution in an insoluble form.[76]

Reactions with lipids. The fat of adipose tissue can be made insoluble in lipid-solvents by prolonged treatment with chromium trioxide,[174], [51] but the ordinary period of fixation does not suffice. The reactions with lipids have not been studied in detail, but they probably resemble those of potassium dichromate (p. 50).

Reactions with carbohydrates. Polysaccharides are converted to aldehydes, by oxidation, and will then respond to colour-tests for aldehydes.[28] It is not certain that chromium trioxide actually fixes glycogen, but the aldehyde formed seems less liable to be dissolved out of the tissues by water than glycogen itself is.

Rate of penetration. Slow ($K = 1 \cdot 0$).

Shrinkage or swelling. Shrinks gelatine-albumin gel slightly, tissues considerably.

Hardening. Moderate.

Method of washing out. It is usual to wash out in running water. If any free chromium trioxide is left in the tissues, it may subsequently be reduced to green chromic oxide, Cr_2O_3, by ethanol or some other reducer. The oxide is difficult to remove from the tissues, as it is insoluble in ordinary solvents and resistant to acids and other reagents.

Effect on the appearance of cells in microscopical preparations. Ground cytoplasm is rather coarsely coagulated and there may be some distortion of the shape of the cell; the nucleus is on the whole well preserved, the chromosomes excellently.

In paraffin sections, cell-aggregates are quite well fixed; so is the nucleus, though the nuclear sap is changed to a coarse coagulum; the chromosomes and nucleolus are particularly well shown; mitochondria and lipid droplets are not seen.

Cytoplasm has a strong affinity for acid dyes and is therefore easily dyed in a different colour from the nucleoprotein, though the latter has not such a strong affinity for basic dyes as it has after fixation by mercuric chloride or formaldehyde.

Compatibility with other fixatives. It can be mixed with mercuric chloride, osmium tetroxide, or acetic acid. If it is mixed with potassium dichromate, the special properties of the latter substance do not appear (see p. 50). As a general rule it is best not to mix chromium trioxide with reducers, such as ethanol or form-aldehyde, with which it reacts. A few useful fixatives, however, contain chromium trioxide and formaldehyde.[1, 166]

CHAPTER 4

Non-Coagulant Primary Fixatives

The non-coagulants form rather a heterogeneous group. Formaldehyde and osmium tetroxide resemble one another in being additive non-coagulants that harden protein gels without separating the water from the protein in them, and fix protoplasm without producing microscopical spongeworks. Potassium dichromate and acetic acid are anomalous. They are not fixatives for simple proteins. The former is used chiefly for its action on certain lipids, the latter for its swelling effect, which counteracts the shrinkage caused by other reagents used in fixation and embedding.

Formaldehyde and osmium tetroxide are of outstanding importance in modern microtechnique. The former is much used in histochemical studies, the latter in electron-microscopy. They will therefore be treated at greater length than the other primary fixatives selected for description in this book.

FORMALDEHYDE

Standard concentration. 4% w/v aqueous solution.

Formula. H_2CO.

Description. Colourless gas; it is very soluble in water as $HO(H_2CO)_nH$. The monomer, $HO(H_2CO)H$, predominates at the standard concentration. The commercial fluid, 'formalin', is approximately at 40% w/v solution, containing some methanol. Polymers predominate in this, and the high polymer, paraformaldehyde ($n = 100$ or more), tends to be deposited as a white precipitate.

Ionization. Formaldehyde itself ionizes to a minute degree, with production of a negligible amount of hydronium ions. It is easily oxidized, however, by atmospheric oxygen to formic acid, and the standard solution, prepared by the dilution of commercial formalin with distilled water, has a pH of about 4. If calcium carbonate is present in excess, the pH is 6·4.[160]

Oxidation-potential. Formaldehyde can be reduced to methanol, and thus may act as an oxidizing agent. Its oxidation potential, however, is lower than that of any other fixative, so far as is known (0·23 volt).

Reactions with proteins. This subject is particularly well understood, because it has been necessary for industrial chemists to study it carefully in connexion with the so-called 'tanning' of leather. It will therefore be treated here at some length.

One of the most effective ways of studying additive fixation is to prepare polypeptides consisting of a single amino-acid many times repeated, and to find how much of the fixative they take up from solution. It is only necessary to know how much polypeptide is present and the initial and final concentrations of the fixative substance. This method has been very successfully used in the study of fixation by formaldehyde. Although no protein consists of a chain composed entirely of similar links, yet some are made up of very few amino-acids, and these also are useful in the study of fixation.

Polyglycine is an artificial polypeptide consisting of nothing but a group of glycine molecules, joined by peptide bonds. Similarly, polyglutamic acid consists of a group of glutamic acid molecules, joined in the same way. The fibroin of silk consists mostly of alanine and tyrosine. All these substances bind very little formaldehyde.[78]

Structural formulae of certain amino-acids, as components of polypeptides and proteins

Polyglutamine is an artificial polypeptide consisting of nothing but a group of glutamine molecules joined by peptide links. This particular polypeptide, in striking contrast to polyglycine, polyglutamic acid, and silk fibroin, binds more formaldehyde than any other macromolecule, so far as is known.[78] A glance at the structural formulae shown here and on p. 19 suggests strongly that the group that binds formaldehyde is the $-NH_2$ of polyglutamine. This conclusion is borne out by experiments made with deaminized proteins; that is to say, with proteins in which the $-NH_2$ groups of polyglutamine and other basic amino-acids have been replaced by $-OH$. These deaminized proteins bind little formaldehyde.

Lysine is the most abundant amino-acid possessing the amino-group, and is thought to be particularly important in fixation by formaldehyde. The reaction might be as follows:

$$-(CH_2)_4NH_2 \quad + \quad H_2CO \quad = \quad -(CH_2)_4NH.H_2COH$$

lysine side-group   *formaldehyde*

The $-OH$ group shown in this equation is reactive, and thus a methylene bridge ($-CH_2-$) can be formed between two protein chains, each possessing an amino-group.

$$-NH-CH_2-NH-$$

A methylene bridge

One can readily imagine two lysine groups on neighbouring protein chains being linked in this way, but analysis shows that there is not a 1:2 relation between the number of molecules of formaldehyde taken up and the number of lysine groups linked to them. It is not probable that two adjacent chains would have many lysine radicles neatly arranged opposite one another, ready to be linked by methylene bridges. Lysine may often in fact be linked to glutamine, or may bind formaldehyde here and there without the formation of a bridge.

Bridge-formation will harden a protein gel, but formaldehyde, as we have seen, is not a coagulant fixative, and it is evident that many of the hydrophil groups retain their relation with water molecules. It is a remarkable experience to transfer a living or fresh jelly-fish from sea-water to formaldehyde solution (preferably dissolved in sea-water) and to see how marvellously its transparency is preserved. This could not happen if the proteins were coagulated. The specimen becomes opaque, however, if after treatment with formaldehyde the water is removed by a dehydrating agent. Similarly, the ground cytoplasm of a cell fixed with formaldehyde loses part of its initial homogeneity when passed through dehydrating agents in the course of paraffin embedding. Formaldehyde does not stabilize the cytoplasm fully against the destructive effects of subsequent dehydration.

Formaldehyde does not coagulate nucleoproteins.

Reactions with nucleic acids. Does not precipitate DNA from solution.

Reactions with lipids. Most lipids are well preserved by formaldehyde, though not necessarily fixed. Triglycerides and cholesterol, for example, are not dissolved. If lipid-solvents are avoided in the subsequent treatment of tissues fixed by formaldehyde, the lipids of adipose tissue remain in their original sites. Certain phospholipids, however, are very slowly dissolved by aqueous solutions of formaldehyde.[90, 126, 184, 44] (Lecithin is not dissolved.) In dissolving, there is a partial separation of glycerophosphoric acid from the nitrogenous base.

Formaldehyde tends to render phospholipids insoluble *in lipid-solvents*.[128, 101, 10] It thus acts as a fixative for lecithin. The chemistry of this process has not been fully worked out, but reaction with the nitrogenous bases has been suggested.[101]

There is some evidence that formaldehyde can also react with unsaturated lipids at the double bonds $\left(\begin{smallmatrix} H & H \\ -C=C- \end{smallmatrix} \right)$ on their fatty acid chains.[185] It would appear that in this reaction formaldehyde acts as an oxidizing agent, with production of aldehyde groups in the lipid. It does not appear to be proved that this change confers insolubility in lipid-solvents.

Reactions with carbohydrates. Glycogen often exists in the cell in intimate relation with protein, and formaldehyde fixes the protein in such a way that this carbohydrate is not easily dissolved out by water.[111] Formaldehyde is therefore a valuable component of fixative mixtures intended for use in studies of glycogen.

Rate of penetration. Fast ($K = 3.6$).

Shrinkage or swelling. Swells gelatine-albumin gel considerably, but leaves the volume of liver almost unchanged.

Hardening. Hardens strongly.

Method of washing out. No special washing out is usually necessary, since formaldehyde is very soluble in water and in ethanol.

Effect on the appearance of cells in microscopical preparations. The form of cells is rather well preserved, though there is a tendency for little blebs of cytoplasm to be nipped off from those directly exposed to the fixative (that is, not protected by overlying cells). Cytoplasm is rendered very finely granular. Mitochondria and lipid droplets are generally well preserved. The nucleus remains remarkably lifelike.

In paraffin sections there is considerable distortion. Cell-aggregates are separated from one another by wide artificial spaces; cytoplasm is shrunk towards nuclei. Mitochondria are sometimes retained; most lipid globules have been dissolved away. The interphase nucleus retains a nearly lifelike appearance, but mitotic and meiotic chromosomes are not well fixed.

Formaldehyde leaves proteins in a state in which they readily take up basic dyes (see p. 90). This follows from the fact that their acidic groups are unaffected by this fixative. Their basic groups, on the contrary, are to a large extent blocked, and the affinity for acid dyes is therefore greatly reduced. If the protein were allowed to take up all the formaldehyde with which it was capable of combining, all affinity for acid dyes would presumably be lost. In practice, however, this stage is not reached, because the reaction between protein and formaldehyde proceeds slowly. If soluble proteins or polypeptides be allowed to react with excess of formaldehyde for 8 hours at 70° C, they take up about one-half of the total amount that they are capable of binding, and the reaction is still incomplete after 24 hours.[78] The binding of formaldehyde is of course even slower at room temperature.

Compatibility with other fixatives. Compatible with ethanol, mercuric chloride, and acetic acid. Reduces osmium tetroxide and potassium dichromate slowly, chromium trioxide quickly.

OSMIUM TETROXIDE

Standard concentration. 1% w/v aqueous solution.

Formula. OsO_4.

Description. Pale yellow molecular (non-ionic) crystals, soluble in water at about 7% w/W (in carbon tetrachloride at about 375% w/W). The crystals melt at 41° C. They begin to sublime at a much lower temperature than this; the gas given off is damaging to the epithelium of the eyes, nose, and mouth. This is by far the most expensive of all primary fixatives (1 g costs £3. 10s.).

Ionization. On solution, it takes up a molecule of water to become hydrogen per-perosmate, H_2OsO_5.[186a] This ionizes to a minute extent to produce hydronium ions and $HOsO_5$. The substance can, however, scarcely be called an acid. Acetic is a very weak acid, yet its ionization constant is well over 20 million times as great as that of hydrogen per-perosmate.

Osmic acid, H_2OsO_4, is not used in fixation.

Oxidation-potential. A moderately strong oxidizer (the 2% solution has o.p. 0·64 volt). On reduction, the brown or blackish hydrated dioxide, $OsO_2.2H_2O$, is left.

Reactions with proteins. Osmium tetroxide gives no coagulum with albumin solution, but on the contrary renders the protein no longer coagulable by ethanol or heat.[34] It sets strong protein solutions into gels, and stabilizes gelatine gels against solution by warm water. It does not coagulate nucleoproteins.

Osmium tetroxide is an additive fixative, but the exact site of its attachment to proteins is not known. It is capable, in certain

Action of osmium tetroxide at the ends of a double bond

circumstances, of simultaneous reaction at both ends of the double bond present in many organic substances.[37, 67] The process is additive.

There are not very many suitable double bonds in proteins, and indeed we have no actual proof that osmium tetroxide reacts with proteins in this way. The evidence does point, however, in this direction.

Most compounds of osmium, other than the tetroxide, are dark or even black, and one can use this fact to find which substances react with the tetroxide and which do not. Of the amino-acids, tryptophane and histidine react strongly, forming dark precipitates.[8] These substances contain double bonds in their five-

Tryptophane   *Histidine*

membered rings. Among the various proteins, the ones that contain a high proportion of tryptophane and/or histidine are particularly reactive with osmium tetroxide. There is a positive correlation between the tryptophane-content of a protein and the capacity of that protein, in the form of an aqueous sol, to be gelled by osmium tetroxide.[150]

The capacity of osmium tetroxide to gel protein sols and to harden and stabilize protein gels (p. 45) would be more comprehensible if it could be shown that separate protein chains were

Osmium acting as a bridge between two ring-compounds
(The latter are shown only in part.)

joined together by this substance. Of this we have no positive evidence, but it has been shown that osmium tetroxide can in fact join certain double-bonded ring-compounds together.[67, 68] The double bond is lost in the process. An extra supply of oxygen is required if this reaction is to occur.

Although reactions of this kind are probably concerned in the fixation of proteins by osmium tetroxide, yet there are indications that others also play a part. Tryptophane and histidine are not the only free amino-acids that form a dark precipitate with osmium tetroxide: cysteine (p. 36) behaves in the same way,[8] yet its side-group possesses no double bond.

There is no reason to believe that tryptophane and histidine play any important part in the colouring of proteins by dyes, yet it is characteristic of the proteins of tissues fixed by osmium tetroxide that they show a remarkable lack of affinity for acid dyes.[21] Since these dyes attach themselves to the $-NH_2$ groups of the side-chains of basic amino-acids (especially lysine, p. 19), there is strong reason to believe that osmium tetroxide somehow blocks these groups. The mechanism of such blocking is, however, unknown. Some proteins that contain a lot of lysine and arginine darken readily with osmium tetroxide, but the protamines, which contain a particularly high proportion of arginine, seem scarcely to darken at room-temperature.[8] It would be unjustifiable to assume that darkening is an invariable concomitant of reaction.

Reactions with nucleic acids. Does not precipitate DNA from solution.[76]

Reactions with lipids. Osmium tetroxide blackens unsaturated lipids of all kinds, but does not attack saturated ones.[3] It is therefore clear that it reacts at the double bonds. Nearly all lipids in organisms are mixtures containing some unsaturated components, and blackening is therefore almost invariable, though it may be very slow.

Osmium tetroxide is soluble in lipids. It may therefore enter a saturated lipid and subsequently be reduced to black osmium dioxide (p. 45) when the tissue is placed in ethanol. It follows that the blackening of a lipid droplet does not necessarily prove that the lipid was unsaturated.

It is an unexplained fact that the conjugated lipids of the tissues, though usually highly unsaturated, are darkened by osmium tetroxide much more slowly than the mixed triglycerides.

If suitable antemedia (p. 73) are used, tissues fixed by osmium tetroxide may be embedded in paraffin without loss of unsaturated lipids. Benzene and chloroform are particularly suitable antemedia for this purpose.[59]

If unsaturated lipid that has been blackened by osmium tetroxide is bleached by hydrogen peroxide, the lipid is set free and is now soluble once more in lipid-solvents, including benzene and chloroform.[59]

After the fixation of tissues by osmium tetroxide, the unfixed (saturated) component of a lipid globule may be dissolved out during dehydration[2, 175] or embedding. The fixed (unsaturated) lipid is then left in a spherical cavity, which it does not fill. It applies itself to the wall of the cavity, and may be seen in optical section under the microscope as a ring, crescent, or 'cap'. These appearances have often been misunderstood.[18]

Reaction with carbohydrates. There appears to be no reaction in the ordinary circumstances of fixation.

Rate of penetration. This is the only fixative, so far as is known, that does not maintain a constant K-value. It penetrates slowly. The K-value during the first 16 hours is 1·0, but during the period 16 to 144 hours it is only 0·31.

Shrinkage or swelling. Gelatine-albumin gel shrinks very slightly. There are no satisfactory figures for tissues and cells, but there seems to be little change of volume.

Hardening. Leaves tissues rather soft.

Method of washing out. Osmium tetroxide is usually washed out with running water, to prevent subsequent reduction in the tissues by ethanol. In preparations for electron-microscopy, however, tissues are sometimes transferred directly from the fixative to 50% or 70% ethanol.

Effect on the appearance of cells in microscopical preparations. Preserves the structure of the living cell better than any other primary or mixed fixative. It might almost be supposed that the cell was still alive.

The fixation is good for methacrylate embedding, but there is very poor resistance to the distortion caused by embedding in paraffin. Cell-aggregates are shrunken, so that wide artificial spaces appear; the tissue tends to crack; the cytoplasm contracts round the nuclei; chromosomes (especially in the first meiotic prophase) are poorly fixed.

Acid dyes, as we have seen (p. 47), scarcely act on tissues fixed by osmium tetroxide. Basic dyes are taken up by both nuclear sap and cytoplasm, and differential dyeing of chromatin is therefore not obtained.

Compatibility with other fixatives. Osmium tetroxide reacts with ethanol and formaldehyde, but is compatible with mercuric chloride, chromium trioxide, and potassium dichromate. These three substances prevent its reduction by daylight.

POTASSIUM DICHROMATE

Standard concentration. 1·5% w/v aqueous solution.

Formula. $K_2Cr_2O_7$.

Description. Orange-red crystals, soluble at about 10% w/v in water.

Ionization. The ions produced by the solution of potassium dichromate are the same as those produced by the solution of chromium trioxide, but the proportions are somewhat different. In particular, the amount of hydronium ion is much less, the pH of the standard solution being about 4·1. The chief ion containing chromium is the dichromate, $[Cr_2O_7]^=$, with some hydrogen chromate, $[HCrO_4]^-$.

Oxidation-potential. This is a strong oxidizer (o.p. 0·79 volt), but not nearly so strong as chromium trioxide.

Reactions with proteins. Potassium dichromate is a non-coagulant of proteins, including nucleoproteins. It very gradually renders egg-white more viscous and eventually transforms it into a weak gel. It gels histones more powerfully.[146] With these exceptions, it seems doubtful whether potassium dichromate can be regarded as a fixative for proteins, in the circumstances of its ordinary use in microtechnique; but it must be remarked that

E

gelatine gel can be rendered insoluble in warm water by the action of potassium dichromate in bright light.

Since chromium trioxide is a vigorous coagulant, it is evident that proteins react quite differently to the chrome anions according to whether the pH is low or not.[189] The 'critical range' of pH is from 3·4 to 3·8.[51] At more acid pH than 3·4, the chrome anions coagulate protein; above 3·8, they do not. Acidified potassium dichromate acts like chromium trioxide, provided that the pH is below 3·4.

It seems probable that unacidified potassium dichromate fixes ground cytoplasm by reaction with the lipid component of lipoproteins, but this subject awaits adequate investigation.

Reactions with nucleic acids. Unacidified potassium dichromate not only does not fix, but actually dissolves DNA.

Reaction with lipids. Potassium dichromate is important in microtechnique chiefly for its fixative effect on certain lipids.

Adipose fat can be rendered insoluble in lipid-solvents by very prolonged treatment with a solution of potassium dichromate.[57] The evidence suggests that the unsaturated lipids are oxidized at the double bonds $\left(\begin{smallmatrix} H & H \\ -C = C- \end{smallmatrix} \right)$; the uptake of chromium is not concerned in the process.[58] The reaction is too slow for practical use.

Lipids that have a double bond near the end of the fatty acid chain furthest from the carboxyl group have a special tendency towards polymerization on oxidation; this is accompanied by lessened solubility in lipid-solvents.

Certain lipids are able to take up chromium from solutions of potassium dichromate, and in so doing to lose their solubility in lipid-solvents. This is additive fixation. With the short post-chroming that is usual in microtechnique (for instance, soaking for 24 hours in a 5% solution of potassium dichromate at 37° C), only phospholipids take up the metal. Colour-tests for chromium will therefore reveal the sites of phospholipids in cells.[11, 12] The way in which chromium links itself to the lipid is uncertain. The phospholipids that occur in nature are highly unsaturated, but it is stated that synthetic saturated ones (such as dipalmitoyl lecithin) are able to take up the metal.[50] It seems probable that chromium attaches itself to the phosphate group, though other suggestions have been made.[111]

The possibility has been mentioned above (p. 50) that potassium dichromate may fix ground cytoplasm by acting on the lipid component.

Reactions with carbohydrates. The unacidified salt is not known to fix any carbohydrate. If acidified, it presumably acts like chromium trioxide (p. 38).

Rate of penetration. Since proteins are neither coagulated nor gelled in the ordinary period of fixation, the rate of penetration cannot be measured by the method adopted with other fixatives. There is no satisfactory information about the rate of penetration of this substance.

Shrinkage or swelling. Gelatine-albumin gel is swollen by potassium dichromate. Whole livers remain unchanged in volume in a 3% solution, but they are subject to severe subsequent shrinkage by ethanol.

Hardening. Tissues are left very soft.

Method of washing out. To avoid the possibility that insoluble chromic oxide (Cr_2O_3) will be precipitated in the tissues through subsequent reduction by ethanol, it is usual to wash out in running water. This reduction does not occur, however, if light be excluded.[182]

Effect on the appearance of cells in microscopical preparations. The cell maintains its form rather well. Mitochondria are preserved, but filamentous ones may be changed into ovoids. The nuclear sap becomes finely granular. The nucleolus shrinks (presumably through loss of RNA).

In paraffin sections there is a shrinkage apart of cell aggregates, with production of artificial spaces; the cytoplasm, though rather homogeneous, is shrunk round the nucleus; mitochondria are retained, but swollen; mitotic and meiotic chromosomes and the heterochromatic segments of the interphase nucleus are unfixed. If the fixative solution is acidified below pH 3·4, the appearance is the same as that given by chromium trioxide.

Both basic and acid dyes act quite strongly. The chromatin,

though unfixed, cannot escape through the nuclear membrane; it distributes itself at random within the nucleus. The colouring of it by basic dyes is therefore not informative. This is an unsuitable fixative for studies of the nucleus and chromosomes (unless acidified).

ACETIC ACID

Standard concentration. 5% v/v aqueous solution.

Formula. $H_3C.COOH$.

Description. A colourless liquid with a pungent smell, miscible with water and ethanol in all proportions. The crystals produced by cooling melt at 16·6° C. The undiluted acid is often called 'glacial', because it is so easily frozen.

Ionization. A very weak acid. The pH at the standard concentration is about 2·3.[106]

Oxidation-potential. Can oxidize by being reduced to acetaldehyde (o.p. 0·77 volt).

Reactions with proteins. It neither coagulates nor gels most proteins; non-additive. It extracts histone from the tissues. A thick precipitate is formed when acetic acid is added to a solution of nucleoprotein. This is attributed to the action of the acetate ion in splitting off DNA from protein.

Reactions with nucleic acids. Precipitates DNA from solution.

Reactions with lipids. In writings on fixation it is often said loosely that lipids are dissolved by acetic acid. It is true that some of them (cholesterol and sphingomyelin, for instance) are soluble in glacial acetic acid; but at the concentrations at which it is used in fixation, acetic acid is not a lipid-solvent. It has, however, no fixative effect on lipids.

Reactions with carbohydrates. Neither fixes nor destroys them.

Rate of penetration. In experiments to determine this, it is necessary to substitute gelatine-nucleoprotein gel for gelatine-albumin, for acetic acid leaves no visible mark to indicate its progress into the latter. It penetrates rapidly ($K = 2·75$).

Shrinkage or swelling. Its capacity to swell protein gels and tissues is the most striking character of acetic acid, and the main reason for its use as a component of fixative mixtures. Its action offsets the shrinkage caused by other substances used in micro-technique. Gelatine-albumin gel expands to between 4 and 5 times its original volume in 18 hours (fig. 5, p. 27). Acetic acid has much more swelling effect than the mineral acids have. This is partly because the pH is not low enough to cause coagulation; partly, it seems, because the undissociated acid is responsible for some of the swelling. Thus, acetic acid has a swelling (or anti-shrinking) effect even when it is used as a constituent of a non-aqueous mixture, such as Clarke (see p. 59). In aqueous media acids are thought to break the salt-links that connect protein chains; the hydrophil groups thus exposed would draw water into the gel or tissue.

Hardening. Leaves tissues much softer than any other fixative does.

Method of washing out. Since acetic acid is miscible with ethanol in all proportions and has no tendency to produce extrinsic artifacts, no special washing out is necessary.

Effect on the appearance of cells in microscopical preparations. The external form of the cell is fairly well preserved. So, in general, are the cytoplasmic inclusions, but the mitochondria become less visible and may disappear. The nuclear contents are transformed into a coarse network.

In paraffin sections, cell-aggregates tend to be widely separated, with artificial spaces in between. Cytoplasm is sometimes coarsely reticular, sometimes contracted round the nuclei. Mitochondria are absent. The nuclear sap is coarsely reticular; the nucleolus is swollen; metaphase and anaphase chromosomes are rather well fixed; the mitotic spindle appears fibrous.

The acetate ion only produces its characteristic fixation-image on the more acid side of pH 4 or thereabouts.[190] On the less acid side there is no fixation and the tissues macerate.

Cytoplasm takes acid dyes strongly, basic ones rather feebly. The chromatin of interphase nuclei colours feebly with basic dyes, scarcely at all with acid ones. Metaphase and anaphase chromosomes colour strongly with basic dyes.

Compatibility with other fixatives. Compatible with all other

fixatives, but potassium dichromate behaves like chromium trioxide if mixed with acetic acid, unless the amount of acid is so
small that the pH is on the less acid side of the critical range
(p. 50).

CHAPTER 5

Practical Fixative Solutions

The only primary fixatives that are commonly used without the admixture of other primaries are formaldehyde and osmium tetroxide. Solutions of primaries used in practice in this way may be called *simple fixatives* to distinguish them from *fixative mixtures*, which contain two or more primaries. Simple fixatives usually contain 'indifferent' or non-fixative salts (p. 29) in addition to the primary. Some of the indifferent salts that are used with formaldehyde and osmium tetroxide will be mentioned in the present chapter.

The great majority of practical fixative solutions are mixtures. The formulae for a very large number of these have been published. It is evident, from a study of the papers in which the formulae first appeared, that most of them were not the product of scientific experiment based on knowledge of the properties of their components. On the contrary, they were put together in a hit-or-miss fashion. In several cases the formula was relegated to a footnote, with no indication of any reasons governing the choice or concentration of the ingredients. Some of these empirical fluids gave good results and found favour, others did not. A process of natural selection of almost random variations resulted in the survival, on the whole, of the fittest; though many that are used are superfluous.

To understand the action of fixative mixtures, it is best to make a careful study of a few valuable ones. The principles involved will emerge, and will be found widely applicable. The mixtures chosen for study in this book are those of Clarke, Zenker, Flemming, Helly, and Altmann.

The reader may care to refer to the general remarks on the period of fixation given on p. 24.

FORMALDEHYDE IN SIMPLE FIXATIVES

When used in this way, formaldehyde is generally dissolved in a solution of an indifferent salt. The latter is used at a concentration that gives the same osmotic pressure as the body-fluids of the organism from which a part is to be taken for fixation, or at a concentration slightly less than this. The following is suitable for the tissues of most vertebrates other than elasmobranchs, and for many terrestrial and fresh-water invertebrates:

Distilled water	.	.	.	83 ml
Sodium chloride, 10% aq.	.	.	.	7 ml
Formalin	.	.	.	10 ml

Keep marble in the fluid. pH (in the presence of marble), 6·0. Wash out with water or 50% ethanol.

In this and other formulae, the word 'formalin' means the commercial fluid containing formaldehyde at approximately 40% w/v. In the fixing solutions given here, formaldehyde is therefore used at its standard concentration.

For the tissues of marine invertebrates, one may dilute formalin with 9 times its volume of sea-water. The pH of the fluid is 7·6.

There can be no doubt that non-fixative salts improve fixation by formaldehyde and certain other primary fixatives. Since they are used at concentrations that give about the same osmotic pressure as the body-fluids of the organism, the fixative solution as a whole is hypertonic, for the osmotic pressure of the formaldehyde or other fixative is added to that of the non-fixative salt. One would therefore expect the latter to cause shrinkage: in fact, however, the virtue of non-fixative salts is that they *reduce* shrinkage. It has already been mentioned (p. 29) that this has never been satisfactorily explained. It has been suggested that when fixatives are used without indifferent salts, the cells in the interior of a piece of tissue behave at first—before the fixative substance itself has arrived—as though the piece had been placed in distilled water: that is to say, they swell up and burst. After bursting, they are thought to shrink, and to be fixed subsequently in this shrunken condition. If an indifferent salt is used, it diffuses into the tissue ahead of the fixative, and prevents the initial swelling and bursting.[187] Certain difficulties in accepting this hypothesis as a complete explanation have been discussed rather fully elsewhere.[21]

Salts used for the purpose just mentioned may play another rôle as well. Phospholipids have a tendency to alter their form by sending out microscopical, tentacle-like 'myelin forms' into surrounding water. Calcium salts prevent this change.[108] In studies of the lipid constituents of cells it is therefore reasonable to substitute calcium chloride for sodium chloride in fixative solutions.[14] The concentration must be made slightly higher than that of sodium chloride, if the same osmotic pressure is to be obtained. The following formula is suitable:

Distilled water	80 ml
Calcium chloride (anh.), 10% aq. . .	10 ml
Formalin	10 ml

Keep marble in the fluid. pH (in the presence of marble), 5·7. Wash out with water or 50% ethanol.

Formaldehyde is much used in these simple solutions in histochemical studies, especially of lipids. To make sure that phospholipids will be fixed, the tissue may be 'postchromed'. After quite short fixation (6 hours) in the formaldehyde solution, it is transferred (without washing) to a solution of potassium dichromate. A solution of this salt maintained at saturation in an incubator at 37° C is suitable. Treatment for a day or two suffices. The tissue must then be washed in running water overnight. More elaborate methods of postchroming are also available.[11, 16]

OSMIUM TETROXIDE IN SIMPLE FIXATIVES

Osmium tetroxide gives excellent results when unmixed with other primary fixatives, provided that a suitable embedding medium, such as methacrylate (p. 77), is used. Gross shrinkage and distortion occur if tissues fixed in this way are embedded in paraffin.[21] There is evidence[139] that the submicroscopical structure of cells is best stabilized if the fixative solution is buffered just on the alkaline side of neutrality, though this has been disputed. The buffer may also act as an indifferent salt. A modification of Michaelis's buffer[123] is usually used, probably because it is not harmful to the cells of most vertebrates. The buffer at pH 7·4 is this:

Sodium acetate and sodium veronal, both

at $\frac{M}{7}$ in one solution, aq. . . . 20 ml

Hydrochloric acid, 0·1 N . . . . 20 ml
Sodium chloride, 8·5 aq. . . . . 8 ml
Distilled water . . . . . 52 ml

The acetate-veronal solution for use in this buffer and in Palade's fixative (see below) is made by dissolving 9·714 g of sodium acetate, $3H_2O$, and 14·714 g of sodium veronal in distilled water, and making up the volume to 500 ml by the addition of distilled water.

Michaelis's buffer has approximately the same osmotic pressure as the body-fluids of mammals. Sodium veronal is a useful constituent of buffers intended for biological work in the neighbourhood of neutrality. Boric-borate buffers are troublesome, because boric acid forms complexes with carbohydrates and all other organic di- and polyhydroxy-compounds. Sodium acetate acts in buffers at a much lower pH than 7·4, and an equally good solution lacking this constituent could probably be devised.

Palade's fixative[139] is Michaelis's buffer at pH 7·4, with the addition of 1 g of osmium tetroxide and the substitution of distilled water for the sodium chloride solution. Thus it contains osmium tetroxide at its standard concentration, and the saline constituents are hypotonic to the body-fluids of mammals. It is convenient to make up Palade's fixative thus:

Sodium acetate and sodium veronal, both

at $\frac{M}{7}$ in one solution (see above) . . 20 ml

Hydrochloric acid, 0·1 N . . . 20 ml
Distilled water . . . . . 10 ml

To 1 ml of the fluid, add 1 ml of 2% osmium tetroxide solution. pH of the fixative solution, 7·4.

Use at about 5° C. Fix pieces not exceeding 1 mm in thickness for 1 to 4 hours. Wash out in several changes of distilled water; or pass directly to 50% or 70% ethanol.

Palade's fixative and variants of it have been enormously used in electron-microscopy, with great success. Since Michaelis's buffer does not precipitate calcium from its salts, it is legitimate to substitute 10 ml of calcium chloride solution for the 10 ml of distilled water used in making up the buffer.[24] The concentration of this solution may be anywhere from 1% to 10% of the anhydrous salt; the final concentration will be from 0·1% to 1%. Calcium chloride is particularly valuable in the study of lipid droplets.[60, 23]

We turn now to fixative mixtures.

CLARKE (1851)[62]

Absolute ethanol	.	.	.	.	. 3 vols
Acetic acid (glacial)		.	.	.	. 1 vol

(The constituents are not ionized and pH has therefore no meaning.) Wash out in absolute ethanol.

The formula for this fixative was given by the English neurologist no less than 35 years before Carnoy, the celebrated Belgian cytologist, first published it.[49] In the intervening period it was familiar in microtechnique as *die Clarke'sche Vorschrift*.[79] This is the most ancient of all fixative mixtures commonly used in microtechnique today.

The advantage that may be gained by mixing certain primary fixatives cannot be more vividly illustrated than by a consideration of Clarke's hardy centenarian. By themselves, ethanol and acetic acid are both very bad fixatives (see pp. 33 and 53), but each compensates neatly for the defects of the other. The shrinkage that ethanol alone would cause is offset by the swelling action of acetic acid; the latter stabilizes nucleoproteins, which are left unfixed by the former; acetic acid fixes neither cytoplasm nor nuclear sap, but both are fixed by ethanol (the former in a rather coarse coagulum). The mixture is admirable in routine micro-anatomy and histology, of some value in studies of chromosomes, and applicable also in histochemistry whenever it is desirable to avoid additive fixation and the resultant shift in the iso-electric points of proteins; glycogen is preserved, but not fixed. The fluid is a solvent of many lipids; for this reason, and because it coagulates rather coarsely, it is unsuitable for the study of most cytoplasmic inclusions.

ZENKER'S FLUID (1894)[188]

Distilled water	.	.	.	.	. 100 ml
Mercuric chloride	.	.	.	.	. 5 g
Potassium dichromate	.	.	.	.	2·5 g
Sodium sulphate	.	.	.	.	. 1 g

To 20 ml, add 1 ml of glacial acetic acid immediately before use. pH 2·5.[52]

Pieces of tissue need not be very small.

If the tissue is to be dehydrated in grades of ethanol, pass it directly from the fixative to 50% ethanol acidified by the addition of 2% v/v of concentrated sulphuric acid;[24] transfer from this to a 0·5% w/v solution of iodine in 70% or 80% ethanol.

If the tissue is to be dehydrated by means of cellosolve (p. 74), pass it directly from the fixative to 50% cellosolve and from this to a 0·5 w/v solution of iodine in undiluted cellosolve.[26]

Zenker's fluid is chosen as our next example after Clarke because it is one of the best fixatives for use in routine histology and in preliminary work with unknown tissues in biological microtechnique of all kinds. It contains two protein coagulants (mercuric chloride and acidified potassium dichromate) and a substance that opposes shrinkage (acetic acid). No non-coagulant fixative of protein is included in the mixture. Sodium sulphate is an 'indifferent' salt; its effect in this mixture is uncertain.

The ground cytoplasm and certain cytoplasmic inclusions are far better preserved by Zenker than by most routine fixatives. The fine texture of the protein coagulate is probably due to the mercuric chloride, which also ensures easy dyeing. Acidified potassium dichromate favours the action of acid dyes, which give much more brilliant effects than after Clarke.

The only notable defect of Zenker is a tendency to crumple collagen fibres.

FLEMMING'S STRONG FLUID (1884)[77]

Distilled water	0·8 ml
Chromium trioxide, 5% aq. . .	0·3 ml
Osmium tetroxide, 2% aq. . .	0·4 ml
Acetic acid, 20% (or less) aq. . .	0·5 ml

As a general rule, use the full concentration of acetic acid.
pH 1·4;[52] the amount of acetic acid used does not affect the pH.[145]
Use pieces 2 mm or less in thickness.
Wash out for several hours in running water or repeated changes.

Since 2 ml of the mixture are sufficient for the fixation of the small pieces of tissue that should be used, it is desirable to follow the formula given above. There is then no wastage of the extremely expensive osmium tetroxide. The fluid made up in this way has the same composition as that which results from the use of Flemming's own formula.

Flemming contains a trio of ingredients that are found over and over again in successful mixtures; namely,

(1) one or more coagulants of protein (in this case chromium trioxide);

(2) a non-coagulant fixative of protein (in this case osmium tetroxide);

(3) acetic acid.

One might suppose that the best results would be given by non-coagulant fixatives in the absence of coagulants; but tissue that has been treated with no other fixative of protein than a non-coagulant does not give ready access to paraffin, and the preparation of good paraffin sections is often difficult. This particularly applies to osmium tetroxide. The spongework produced by coagulants provides spaces into which melted paraffin can enter (p. 75). Beyond this, coagulants give the best fixation of chromosomes, and chromium trioxide is pre-eminent in this respect. If, however, no non-coagulant fixative of proteins is included, the spongework tends to be unduly coarse, and cytoplasmic inclusions are distorted mechanically or even destroyed. The coagulants and non-coagulants thus compensate for one another's defects.

The chief effect of acetic acid in these mixtures is the prevention of excessive shrinkage. Tissues fixed in acetic acid alone swell, but are greatly shrunken on subsequent dehydration. If, however, they are stabilized in the swollen condition by the simultaneous action of a fixative for proteins, the shrinkage seen in the final preparation is far less. When acetic acid is used in mixtures at 5% or thereabouts, there is no necessity to add an indifferent salt. Acetic acid also plays a part in the fixation of nucleoprotein, but this is not important when the coagulant is chromium trioxide.

A defect of Flemming is that the constituents penetrate at different speeds. The most external part of the piece of tissue is not capable of being dyed successfully, because osmium tetroxide has exerted too powerful an effect upon it (p. 49); the most internal part shows the effects of fixation by chromium trioxide and acetic acid alone (apart from the blackening of lipid globules). In the intermediate region, however, fixation is usually excellent. Chromosomes are well fixed, as indeed one would expect; for the famous German cytologist who designed the mixture did more than anyone else to clarify the process of mitosis. The ground cytoplasm preserves much of its homogeneity; various cytoplasmic inclusions, especially the idiozome, are very well shown. Mitochondria are not necessarily destroyed, but as a rule they are not easily shown after fixation by Flemming with full acetic. In the study of these particular cytoplasmic inclusions the acetic acid is commonly much reduced in amount[32] or omitted.[109, 16]

HELLY (1903)[97]

Distilled water	.	.	.	.	100 ml
Mercuric chloride	.	.	.	5 g
Potassium dichromate	.	.	.	2·5 g
Sodium sulphate	.	.	.	.	1 g

To 10 ml add 0·5 ml of formalin (neutralized by marble) immediately before use.

pH 3·7.[52]

The fixative may be washed out in acidified 50% ethano land iodized

70% or 80% ethanol, in the same way as Zenker's fluid. Alternatively, transfer the tissue directly from the fixative to a saturated solution of potassium dichromate maintained at 37° C, leave for 24 to 48 hours, wash overnight in running water, and dehydrate with through grades of ethanol, with iodine treatment.

The Viennese anatomist's fixative is one of the most valuable in the routine study of cytoplasmic inclusions in paraffin sections. It contains a coagulant and a non-coagulant fixative of protein (mercuric chloride and formaldehyde respectively), and also an important fixative of many lipids (unacidified potassium dichromate). It is uncertain whether the indifferent salt (sodium sulphate) plays a useful rôle in the mixture.

Helly is not nearly so similar to Zenker as the list of its constituents might suggest. Formaldehyde and unacidified potassium dichromate are profoundly different in their effects on tissues from acetic acid and acidified potassium dichromate.

Mercuric chloride and formaldehyde, acting in conjunction, fix ground cytoplasm smoothly, giving just sufficient sponginess to allow easy penetration by paraffin. The constituents penetrate well and it is not necessary to use very small pieces.

Postchroming is useful in studies of mitochondria. The latter are usually well fixed, though those of mammalian liver tend to shorten and round up.

ALTMANN (1894)[3]

Osmium tetroxide, 2% aq. . . . 1 vol.
Potassium dichromate, 5% aq. . . 1 vol.

pH 4·0.[52]

Use pieces of tissue 2 mm or less in thickness. In studies of mitochondria fix for 24 hours (postchroming is unnecessary).

Wash out overnight in running water.

Altmann was the first serious student of mitochondria, though he did not know them under this name. The distinguished Leipzig cytologist was mistaken about the nature of these cytoplasmic inclusions, which he regarded as 'elementary organisms', living within the cell; but he designed a fixative that is still one of the best for showing them in preparations for light-microscopy.

The fluid differs from the mixtures already described and from the great majority of fixative mixtures used in microtechnique, in containing no coagulant. Ground cytoplasm is therefore fixed very homogeneously. The cytoplasmic inclusions maintain their form, partly because they are not distorted by coagulation of the surrounding ground cytoplasm, partly because both the constituents of the fluid are lipid-fixatives. The dichromate, a stronger oxidizer than osmium tetroxide, prevents excessive blackening of the tissues and gives easy colouring by acid dyes; unfortunately it dissolves nucleoprotein, and the fixative is not adapted to studies of nucleus or chromosomes.

The disadvantage of this fixative is that it does not give ready access to melted paraffin. Embedding often results in shrinkage and distortion, the tissue cracks, and sections are difficult to flatten. When skill or luck overcomes these troubles, excellent preparations result.

Ammonium dichromate may be substituted for potassium dichromate in this solution.[26] The pH of 'NH₄-Altmann' is slightly more acid. The ammonium salt differs curiously from the other.[189] Mitochondria are not well fixed at the surface of the piece of tissue, but in the interior they are better fixed than by potassium dichromate: filamentous ones retain their form, instead of shortening and thickening. For this reason it is best to cut out rather large pieces of tissue when the ammonium salt is to be used.

The great majority of fixative mixtures fall into one or other of four groups. Fifteen of the most valuable are listed here.

Group A. **Coagulant + acetic acid.** These are primarily fixatives for micro-anatomy and histology. Examples: Clarke,[62] Zenker.[188]

Group B. **Coagulant + non-coagulant + acetic acid.** These are mostly fixatives for detailed histology and general cytology: many are used in the study of chromosomes. Examples: Flemming's strong fluid,[77] Allen's 'B.15',[1] Bouin,[39] Heidenhain's 'Susa',[96] Hermann (mammalian formula),[98] Sanfelice.[166]

Group C. **Coagulant + non-coagulant.** These are routine fixatives for cytoplasmic inclusions. Examples: Helly,[97] Champy,[55a] Lewitsky-saline,[109], [16] Mann,[115] Zenker-without-acetic.

Group D. **Non-coagulants only.** This is a small group, adapted to the study of cytoplasmic inclusions. Examples: Altmann,[3] Regaud.[156]

It is curious that so many valuable fixative mixtures contain one or more coagulants. This is probably connected with the predominance of paraffin as an embedding medium. Group D is likely to come to the fore in the future, as new plastics replace paraffin; but it remains to be seen whether any non-coagulant is as useful as chromium trioxide in the fixation of chromosomes for light-microscopy.

CHAPTER 6

Embedding

In the early days of histology and cytology, sections were cut by hand. Skilled workers could cut ordinary plant tissue admirably, for each cell was held in place by a firm cell-wall. Zoologists were at a disadvantage, which they sought to overcome by using fixatives that hardened the tissues. Indeed, their attention was focused on this, rather than on the primary object of fixation; and accordingly they called their fixatives hardening agents. When microtomes came into general use, it was found convenient to embed tissues in suitable media which would hold the cells and intercellular matter in place while the razor slid past them. Animal tissues are seldom sectioned today without having been embedded, and it is therefore unnecessary that fixatives should have a hardening effect.

Embedding media must necessarily be substances that are capable of easy conversion from liquid to solid form. The liquid penetrates the tissues to a greater or lesser extent and is then converted into a solid. We shall see that this conversion may involve hydrogen bonding, covalent linkage, crystallization, or polymerization.

It is sometimes suggested that embedding media may be divided into two groups: those that penetrate the cells, and those that merely surround them. Actually, it is doubtful whether any sharp distinction can be drawn. Some embedding media certainly enter cells, and indeed may penetrate their nuclei (p. 75); but whether any particular medium penetrates any particular kind of cell or merely surrounds it may depend on the fixative used. Those fixatives that coagulate proteins in the form of a coarse spongework leave the tissues in a state that favours the entry of embedding media. Those that fix homogeneously, without coagulation, tend to render the internal parts of cells inaccessible to most embedding media. Failure to enter cells by no means necessarily renders an embedding medium useless, for it may enter inter-cellular spaces and give considerable support during sectioning.

Three substances have been chosen to represent different sorts of embedding media. These three are gelatine, paraffin wax, and butyl methacrylate. They have been chosen partly because they illustrate three very different processes of solidification, partly because they are among the most valuable of all embedding media.

GELATINE

The outstanding advantage of gelatine as an embedding medium is that the tissues need not at any stage be dehydrated. It follows that most lipids, even if unfixed, remain in the tissue and can be coloured by lysochromes (p. 86). Distortion by dehydration is also avoided. There are, however, several disadvantages in gela-tine embedding, as ordinarily practised. The gelatine cannot be removed from the tissue; and since it is capable of taking up both basic and acid dyes, it often tends to obscure the view. The ordinary process cannot be relied on to provide sections thinner than about 5 μ, and they do not adhere to form ribbons. It has recently been claimed, however, that by modifying the procedure one may obtain ribbons of sections only 20 mμ thick, suitable for examination with the electron-microscope.[84]

It is commonly supposed that there is some special virtue in formaldehyde that makes this the fixative of choice when tissues are to be embedded in gelatine, but in fact almost any fixative may be used. It is reasonable as a general rule to avoid those that dissolve lipids.

To prepare tissues for embedding in gelatine, it is only neces-sary to wash out the fixative, generally with running water. If the fixative was one that fixes gelatine as well as the proteins of the tissues, it is important to get rid of it by thorough washing; for otherwise it would fix the gelatine as it started to diffuse into the tissue, and thus stop its progress. Among the common primary fixatives, however, only formaldehyde and osmium tetroxide fix gelatine.

Gelatine is a chemically modified form of collagen, an insoluble protein distinguished by its high content of glycine, proline, and hydroxyproline.

$$
\begin{array}{l}
\text{N—CH}_2 \\
\quad\quad\ \text{CH}_2 \\
\text{HC—CH}_2 \\
\quad\ \text{C}{=}\text{O} \\
\quad\ |
\end{array}
$$

Proline as part of a protein chain

(*The middle* ⟩CH$_2$ group is replaced by

⟩CH.OH in hydroxyproline.)

The collagen used in the preparation of gelatine is derived from the organic matter in the bones of cattle and from the white connective tissue fibres in the skin of cattle and pigs. Bones are first decalcified with hydrochloric acid. The skin or bone is 'limed' for several weeks in an aqueous solution of calcium hydroxide; the soluble proteins are thus dissolved away. After having been washed with water, the material that has resisted solution is kept in clean water at about 60° C for several hours. In this it dissolves. It is filtered, cooled to produce a gel, and dried.[102] The dry material is sold in the form of sheets or powder. The latter is the more convenient form for use in the laboratory.

The transformation that is undergone by collagen during the long treatment with limewater is reflected in the change of the iso-electric point from about pH 7·8 to pH 4·7.[88] This results from the conversion of amide-groups in the asparagine and glutamic acid of the protein chain to the carboxyl groups of aspartic acid and glutamic acid respectively. It is this change that makes gelatine so much more readily colourable by basic dyes than collagen is. Various bonds that tie the protein chains together, such

$$\begin{array}{c} \text{NH} \\ | \\ \text{HC.CH}_2\text{.C} \overset{\displaystyle \text{O}}{\underset{\displaystyle \text{NH}_2}{\diagup}} \\ | \\ \text{C}=\text{O} \\ | \end{array}$$

$$\begin{array}{c} | \\ \text{NH} \\ | \\ \text{HC.CH}_2\text{.C} \overset{\displaystyle \text{O}}{\underset{\displaystyle \text{OH}}{\diagup}} \\ | \\ \text{C}=\text{O} \\ | \end{array}$$

Asparagine as part of
a protein chain

Aspartic acid as part of
a protein chain

as those between carboxyl in one chain and basic groups in
another,[88] are also broken by the alkaline bath. When the
material is warmed, the loosened chains move apart from one
another, and are shortened by hydrolytic transverse breakage of
the peptide links.[122] Chains varying in molecular weight from
about 15,000 to 45,000 are thus set free in association with water
as a sol. The molecules are neither fully extended into rods nor
compacted into globular form, but each is about 50 times as long
as broad.

When the filtered sol is cooled, these molecules attach themselves to one another, probably by hydrogen bonding between
peptide groups in previously separate molecules.[88] The bond is

$$\begin{array}{c c} | & | \\ \text{C}=\text{O} & \text{HCR} \\ | & | \\ \text{NH} \cdot \cdot \cdot \text{O}=\text{C} \\ | & | \\ \text{HCR} & \text{NH} \\ | & | \\ \text{C}=\text{O} & \text{HCR} \\ | & | \end{array}$$

A hydrogen bond (.   .) between two peptide groups
in protein chains

very susceptible to heat. Over a wide range of concentration,
gelatine associates with water to form a solid (gel) below 20° C,
a fluid (sol) above 35° C, and a substance showing anomalous
viscosity (neither a solid nor a true fluid) between certain temperatures intermediate between 20° C and 35° C. There are said
to be some free molecules even in the gel.[122]

If gelatine be maintained for a long time at a temperature exceeding 60° C, and especially if it be boiled, the shortening of the protein chain goes so far that the capacity to form a gel on cooling is destroyed. The resulting substance is called metagelatine. Gelatine gels that are intended for embedding should not be melted frequently, since this also has a softening effect.

A piece of fixed tissue that has been washed in water may be transferred directly to a gelatine gel melted at 37° C. There is no reason, either theoretical or practical, why tissue should first be placed in a melted gel of low gelatine content and then transferred to a more concentrated one. A suitable gel may be made by placing 25 g of powdered gelatine in 100 ml of distilled water, and leaving this in an incubator at 37° C until the gelatine has dissolved.

If the gel is to be kept in stock, it is necessary to take precautions against the growth of bacteria and moulds. A good disinfectant for the purpose is sodium p-hydroxybenzoate, since this is particularly effective in preventing the growth of the bacterium that liquefies gelatine gels. It should be dissolved at 0·2% in distilled water, and the gel made with this in place of distilled water.[14]

A gelatine gel that has been formed by simple cooling is scarcely hard enough to give the necessary support to embedded tissue, and sections cut from it are inconveniently sticky. It is possible to harden the gel by slow evaporation,[84] but the usual method is to link the molecules more securely together by the action of fixatives. Formaldehyde is suitable. It will be remembered that it acts by forming methylene bridges between protein chains (p. 42). When the covalent bonds of these bridges have added their effect to that of the hydrogen bonds, the gel is harder; it no longer melts on being warmed, and the tendency to swell in acid solutions is greatly reduced. Sections are still slightly sticky, however. The salts of aluminium are able to fix gelatine. Potassium alum (p. 119) is suitable. It abolishes stickiness and gives hard blocks; but it cannot be used alone, instead of formaldehyde, because sections of gelatine hardened in this way roll up instead of remaining flat. 'Formalum'[14] is a suitable solution for hardening gelatine gels. It is made by diluting commercial formalin with 4 times its volume of a 5% aqueous solution of potassium alum crystals. Gelatine blocks may be preserved indefinitely in formalum.

Formaldehyde solution should be used without the addition of alum if for any reason it is necessary to avoid the mordanting effect of aluminium salts (for instance, in the acid haematein test[11] for phospholipids; on the subject of mordanting, see p. 110).

Beyond hydrogen bonding and the formation of covalent links, a third hardening process is generally used before sections are cut. The water contained in the fixed gelatine is frozen, usually by allowing carbon dioxide at a low temperature to flow past the block. If, however, the gelatine gel has been hardened by evaporation, little water remains in it and the block can be cut with a glass knife without cooling below room-temperature.[84]

It is possible to attach gelatine sections to glass slides,[10] but it is simpler to dye them (or to treat them with lysochromes) while they are still loose. If loose sections are mounted in an aqueous mounting medium, such as dilute glycerine (p. 128) or Farrants's medium (p. 129), the tissue will have been kept continuously wet with water from the moment when the cells were still alive.

PARAFFIN

Solid paraffin (so-called paraffin 'wax') is more commonly used than any other embedding medium. It certainly has great advantages. The process of embedding is quick and simple; embedded material may be stored indefinitely in the dry condition; sections may be obtained regularly at all necessary thicknesses from about 2 μ upwards, if suitable waxes are chosen; and each section adheres automatically to the next as it comes off the microtome knife, so that ribbons are formed. These qualities make paraffin the best embedding medium for most purposes in micro-anatomy and routine histology, and it plays an important part also in studies of chromosomes and other cellular constituents that are not easily distorted or dissolved. The main disadvantages of this medium are the shrinkage that occurs during embedding, and the solution of most lipids. Indeed, the incompleteness of our knowledge of the lipid constituents of cells must be attributed largely to the popularity of paraffin among microtomists.

To prepare tissues for infiltration by melted paraffin wax, it is necessary to dehydrate them thoroughly and soak them in a fluid that is readily miscible with the embedding medium. Ethanol and cellosolve are particularly suitable dehydrating agents.

If all the constituents of the fixative are freely soluble in or miscible with 50% ethanol, the tissue may be transferred directly to that fluid. If one or more of the constituents of the fixative react with ethanol to produce insoluble material, it is usual to wash the tissue thoroughly in running water after fixation. Chromium trioxide, for instance, tends to be reduced by ethanol to insoluble green chromic oxide, Cr_2O_3; osmium tetroxide to black or brown dioxide (OsO_2 or $OsO_2.2H_2O$). It is worth remarking, however, that tissues fixed in chromium trioxide solution may be transferred directly to 50% ethanol, if 2% v/v of strong sulphuric acid has previously been added to the alcoholic solution.[24]

It is customary to transfer tissues through a series of aqueous alcoholic solutions of higher and higher ethanol content, until absolute ethanol is reached. A suitable series is 50%, 80%, 96%, absolute. Many more grades than these are often used, and special apparatus has been invented to achieve very gradual dehydration. It is doubtful whether any benefit accrues from this. However closely graded the series of ethanol solutions may be, there is always considerable shrinkage at one concentration or another, somewhere between 60% and 90% ethanol.[21] It is a useful experience to judge the appearances of dyed and mounted sections of tissues that have been dehydrated in different ways. A friend may be asked to fix two pieces of the same organ in the same fixative, and to dehydrate them in two different ways: one piece through a closely graded series of ethanols, the other through a coarsely graded series, or even from the washing water directly to absolute ethanol. If he makes a number of slides from each piece of tissue and does not divulge which is which, it will be found difficult or impossible to guess.

If the fixative contained mercuric chloride, iodine should be dissolved at 0·5% w/v in one of the grades of ethanol (for instance, 80%), to prevent the formation of a black deposit (p. 36).

If the fixative contained no water (Clarke, p. 59, for instance), the tissue should simply be washed in absolute ethanol.

Although the tissue has now been dehydrated, it cannot be invaded by melted paraffin wax, because ethanol and paraffin are immiscible. It is necessary that the tissue should pass through a fluid that is freely miscible with both. Antemedia[7] are fluids in which tissues are soaked immediately before they are transferred to embedding media. Some of them have about the same refractive index as dehydrated protein. Since they fill up the spaces in the tissue not occupied by dehydrated protein, they render it more or less optically homogeneous and transparent. They are therefore often called 'clearing' agents, but the capacity to 'clear' is a useless attribute of certain antemedia, and some of the best do not possess it. A large number of more or less harmless fluids are miscible with both ethanol and melted paraffin, and one may choose one's antemedium from among them. Toluene is as good as any for routine use. This light, colourless liquid is so called because it was first obtained by distillation of an oleo-resin

CH_3

Toluene

exported from Tolu in Colombia; but nowadays it is got from coal tar. Its boiling-point (110° C) is well above the melting-point of paraffin wax. Tissues tend to be distorted (unevenly shrunk) when passed directly from ethanol to toluene, and it is therefore better to pass them instead to a mixture of ethanol and toluene in equal volumes, and from this to pure toluene.

Ethylene glycol mono-ethyl ether ('cellosolve') may be used instead of ethanol as a dehydrating agent. The relationship of this substance to ethylene glycol (the familiar 'anti-freeze') is shown by the structural formulae. It is made by the action of

$$\begin{array}{ccc}
\text{HO—CH}_2 & \text{CH}_2 & \text{HO—CH}_2 \\
| & \diagup & | \\
& \text{O} & \\
| & \diagdown & | \\
\text{HO—CH}_2 & \text{CH}_2 & \text{C}_2\text{H}_5\text{O—CH}_2 \\
\textit{Ethylene glycol} & \textit{Ethylene oxide} & \textit{Cellosolve}
\end{array}$$

ethanol on ethylene oxide under pressure at high temperature. It is a colourless, odourless liquid boiling at 134° C.[102] It has remarkable powers of dissolving diverse substances, including cellulose nitrate and acetate (whence, presumably, its trade name). It is miscible with water and with toluene in all proportions.

Since cellosolve is a less violent dehydrating agent than ethanol, there is no advantage in using a graded series of mixtures of cellosolve with water. Fixed tissues may be transferred from water to a mixture of cellosolve with an equal volume of water, and then to absolute cellosolve; indeed, it is possible to omit the intermediate stage. If the fixative contained mercuric chloride, iodine should be dissolved at 0·5% in the cellosolve; it must subsequently be washed out by the pure solvent. Tissues pass from absolute cellosolve to a mixture of this with an equal volume of toluene, and thence to toluene itself.

Cellosolve causes less shrinkage and hardening than ethanol. Indeed, there are some organs, such as mucous glands, that can scarcely be sectioned in paraffin after dehydration by ethanol, but present no difficulty when cellosolve is used instead. The great solvent power of this substance is, however, a drawback for certain kinds of work. It appears to dissolve some of the constituents of mitochondria, even when appropriate fixatives have been used.[26] In studies of cytoplasmic inclusions it is safer to pass tissues through ethanol, unless it has been shown that the use of cellosolve is not harmful.

Tissues may be transferred directly from toluene to melted paraffin. It would not appear that there is any advantage in soaking them first in a solution of paraffin in the antemedium.[7]

Paraffin waxes are constituents of crude petroleum. They are saturated, long-chain hydrocarbons of the methane series. The commercial products are mixtures of molecules of different molecular weights. The waxes commonly used in microtechnique melt at various temperatures between 52° and 60° C. This suggests that the number of carbon atoms in most of the molecules is less than 30, for $H_3C(CH_2)_{28}CH_3$ melts at 66° C.

Paraffin wax should be maintained at a temperature only a few degrees C above its melting-point. A wax of high melting-point (that is, with long molecules) should be chosen if thin sections are required, or if the microtome is to be used in a warm room. There is no advantage in transferring tissues first to a wax of low melting-point and then to one of high. Indeed, the wax of low melting-point would be ousted from the tissue by the other wax very slowly and probably incompletely, for these large molecules replace one another slowly by diffusion.

When the tissue is placed in melted paraffin, the antemedium passes out to mix with it, while the separate paraffin molecules diffuse in to replace them. Great shrinkage of the tissue will occur if the antemedium escapes much more quickly than it can be replaced. If, on the contrary, it escapes too slowly (because it is insufficiently soluble in or miscible with paraffin), replacement is likely to be incomplete. Toluene possesses neither of these defects.

It is best to change the melted paraffin once or twice, in order to get rid of the antemedium that has escaped from the tissue and thus to facilitate the escape of the remainder and its replacement by paraffin.

Tissues are much more fully permeated by paraffin than by gelatine. The embedding medium enters the cells, and indeed there is proof that it sometimes penetrates their nuclei: for paraffin crystals, being birefringent, advertise their presence when sections are examined in polarized light.[135] Penetration takes place readily if the proteins of the cells have been coagulated, but with difficulty if they have been fixed homogeneously. It is partly for this reason, in all probability, that coagulant fixatives have retained their popularity, despite the fact that they necessarily distort the finer structure of the cell. Protoplasm that has been fixed by osmium tetroxide is scarcely porous, and paraffin molecules cannot enter freely. As a result the embedded tissue, being dry, friable, and not properly supported, often cracks or crumbles during sectioning.

When replacement of the antemedium is complete, the paraffin is hardened by crystallization on cooling. Each long molecule places itself parallel with its neighbours. The molecules are not fully extended, for each forms a zigzag in one plane.[122] Crystallization occurs readily because the molecules, unlike those of certain other waxy constituents of petroleum, have no major branches that would interfere with close packing. Not every molecule has a branch; such branches as occur arise near one end of the molecule, and are usually only one carbon atom long.[102]

The crystals take the form of plates or needles. Each molecule is held in position only by van der Waals forces, and this accounts for the softness of the material and its low melting-point. There is a tendency to a lamellar structure in the crystal, for all the molecular zigzags lie in parallel planes, and each molecule in each monomolecular plane is somewhat more strongly attracted to its neighbours in that plane than to the molecules of other planes.[122] It is presumably the slipping of the planes on one another that gives paraffin waxes their greasy feel.

It is generally believed that paraffin blocks should be cooled quickly, by plunging them into cold water. The wax then hardens in the form of small crystals, and these are supposed to give better cutting qualities than large crystals. An experiment was performed to test this belief. The kidney of a mouse was cut in two. Both the pieces were fixed in Zenker, dehydrated in ethanol, and passed through toluene into melted wax. One piece of wax was cooled suddenly, in the usual way. The cooling of the other was done in stages: first an hour at 45° C, then an hour at 37° C, then further cooling in a warm room (22° C). Both pieces were cut on the same microtome and the sections dyed and mounted. The two blocks cut equally well and the final preparations were indistinguishable.[26]

Sections of tissue that have been thoroughly permeated by paraffin may be freely exposed to the air without risk of damage. This makes it easy to stick them to glass slides, and as a result paraffin sections are very seldom dyed in the loose state. Egg-white is an excellent adhesive for this purpose. It is best to make a stock solution by diluting it with an equal volume of 1% aqueous sodium chloride solution; any insoluble material is thrown down by centrifuging. In the presence of sodium p-hydroxy-benzoate at 0·2% w/v, this solution resists the attack of bacteria and moulds and may be kept for an indefinite period.[25] For use, the stock solution is diluted with about 50 times its volume of distilled water. The fluid is then spread on a glass slide and the section floated on it. The slide is warmed on a hot plate sufficiently to soften but not melt the paraffin, and any folds in the section flatten out. The water is then drained off as far as possible and the slide left on the hot plate to dry. When it has dried, the minute quantity of albumen between the section and the glass suffices to stick them firmly together.

Glycerine is often mixed with egg-white in the preparation of the adhesive.[117] It serves no purpose.[25]

To remove the paraffin from the dried slide, it is only necessary to soak it for a few minutes in xylene. The slide is then passed through absolute ethanol to 90% and then 70%. If the dye that is to be used is dissolved in a weak ethanol solution, the slide may be transferred to it from 70% ethanol; if the dye is dissolved in water, it is best to rinse in distilled water first.

BUTYL METHACRYLATE

Butyl methacrylate was introduced into microtechnique as an embedding medium in 1949.[137] Although modern plastics of other kinds have been tried since then and one or two of them are promising, yet the methacrylates are still among the best, at any rate for routine use.

The great advantages of this embedding medium are that it causes little distortion and permits sections to be cut at any thickness from 8 μ or more down to about 10 mμ (though for very thin sections a mixture of butyl and methyl methacrylates is used). If tissues are suitably fixed, sectioned in butyl methacrylate at about 3 μ, and mounted in an appropriate medium (p. 128), the appearance of the cells is astonishingly lifelike. Methacrylate is seldom used when sections are to be dyed. It finds its chief application in the preparation of very thin sections for electron-microscopy. The main disadvantage of methacrylate is that the process of embedding is rather complicated.

Very small pieces of tissue (often about 1 cubic mm) are generally used. A solution of osmium tetroxide, buffered at about pH 7·4, is the most usual fixative (p. 58). After fixation the tissue may be washed with distilled water (though many workers use weak ethanol solutions), and must then be dehydrated. Graded ethanols are used for this purpose. It has not been found necessary, even for the most delicate work, to use a closely graded series of ethanols. The series recommended for use in paraffin embedding (50%, 80%, 96%, absolute) is suitable. No special antemedium is required. The tissue may be transferred to a mixture of equal volumes of absolute ethanol and methacrylate, or directly to methacrylate itself.

The embedding medium to which the tissue is transferred is *n*-butyl methacrylate, in monomeric form. This is a colourless, mobile liquid, boiling at about 163° C. It has a distinctive, rather unpleasant smell. The vapour is somewhat toxic and it is desirable to increase the ventilation if the smell is noticeable. Butyl methacrylate is miscible with absolute ethanol and with lipid-solvents such as carbon tetrachloride, acetone, and toluene. It is insoluble in water, on which it floats. It is highly inflammable.

The acrylic acids form a series similar to the fatty acids, but two of the carbon atoms in the chain are joined by a double bond. In the strict sense the series includes only those acids in which the double bond is in the same position, in relation to the carboxyl group, as in acrylic acid itself: that is to say, just beyond

Acrylic acid

Acrylic acid as a segmer in a polymer

the next carbon atom from the carboxyl carbon. The aldehyde corresponding to acrylic acid is acrolein, and from this excessively pungent substance the acid derives its name.

From our point of view, the important character of the acrylic acids is their strong tendency to polymerize, and in doing so to become solids possessing special characters.[102, 158] Polymerization occurs by the addition of one molecule to another, the double bond becoming single in the process. There is no condensation: each repeated unit or 'segmer' consists of the same atoms as the monomer. The substance formed is thus an addition-polymer.

The hydrogen of the carboxyl group of the acrylic acids can be replaced by methyl, ethyl, or other alkyl groups, without loss of the tendency of the molecule to polymerize. The esters thus formed are of greater practical value than the simple monomers. Reaction (in a roundabout way) with normal butyl alcohol, $HO(CH_2)_3CH_3$, gives n-butyl acrylate. This, when polymerized, is a very soft, rubbery substance, not adapted to the purposes of microtomy. If, however, a methyl group be substituted for the hydrogen attached to the next carbon to that of the carboxyl group, a marked change occurs in the physical consistency of the

A segmer of n-butyl acrylate polymer

A segmer of n-butyl methacrylate polymer

polymer. We now have, in n-butyl methacrylate polymer, a hard, colourless, transparent solid, admirably adapted to our needs. All the methacrylates are harder than the corresponding acrylates, but the length of the esterifying alcohol also affects the hardness. The shorter the alcohol, on the whole, the harder the polymer. Methyl methacrylate—better known under its commercial name of perspex—is the hardest of all. It is often used as an embedding-medium for electron-microscopy, usually with the admixture of butyl methacrylate. The latter by itself, however, gives good sections for electron-microscopy as well as for light-microscopy.

If the segmers of butyl methacrylate were only capable of linking together in the way previously mentioned, the substance produced would resemble a fibre rather than a resin. In fact, the long chains branch and link in such a way as to form a three-dimensional spongework devoid of any particular orientation. The reactions involved in this process are mentioned below (p. 82). It is this submicroscopic structure of the methacrylates that fits them so well for use as embedding media, capable of being sectioned equally well in any direction.

At room-temperature the monomer very slowly undergoes spontaneous polymerization. An inhibitor must be added to enable the methacrylate to be stored in monomeric form. Quinone is suitable. It is stated to react with chain-forming radicles to produce stable compounds.[35] Manufacturers add a small proportion of hydroquinone to methacrylate, and this

Hydroquinone   *Quinone*

becomes converted to quinone by spontaneous oxidation. When the methacrylate is about to be used, the inhibitor is removed by shaking the fluid with an aqueous solution of sodium hydroxide. The water, coloured by the inhibitor, separates from the methacrylate under the influence of gravity. The monomer is washed free from sodium hydroxide by being shaken several times with distilled water; the latter is then removed by the addition of anhydrous sodium sulphate. Although uninhibited, the material will remain unpolymerized for many weeks if kept in a refrigerator maintained near 0° C.

The methacrylate is now ready to receive the tissue. The molecules being fairly small, thorough penetration takes place quite easily. The fluid is changed a few times to get rid of the ethanol. It would then gradually harden by polymerization, if left at room-temperature, but the process is too slow for practical use. It is necessary to add an activator or so-called catalyst and to warm to about 60° C. The name 'catalyst' is inaccurate, for, as we shall see, the substance in question forms part (though a very small part) of the hardened material.

The extremely active substance that promotes polymerization is the free phenyl radicle, H_5C_6. It will be remembered that free radicles differ from the vast majority of chemical compounds in possessing an uneven number of electrons in the sum-total of their constituent atoms. In the formulae shown here, it will be

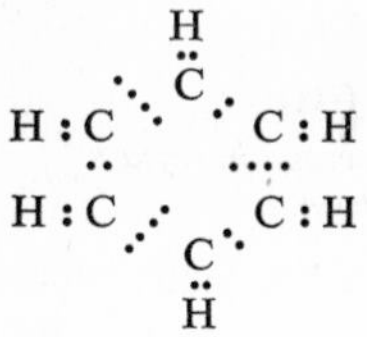

Diagram of the structure of benzene, showing the valency-electrons

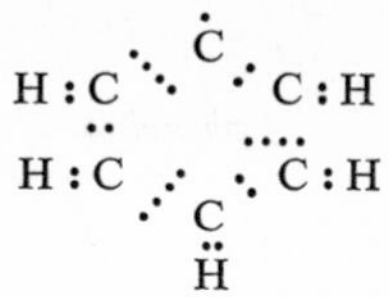

Comparable diagram of the structure of the free phenyl radicle

noticed that 8 electrons of the outer shell are associated with each carbon atom in benzene, but only 7 with one of the carbon atoms in the free phenyl radicle. The formula for the latter is conveniently written $H_5C_6\cdot$ to remind the reader of the existence of the unpaired electron.

Benzoyl peroxide, $(C_6H_5CO)_2O_2$, is used to produce the free phenyl radicle. This colourless, crystalline solid may be regarded as hydrogen peroxide in which each of the hydrogen atoms has been replaced by benzoyl, $C_6H_5CO^-$. It is an explosive, and care should be taken not to grind it with metal instruments; for storage it is damped with water. The tissue is transferred from the unmixed monomer to a weak, freshly prepared solution of benzoyl peroxide in the monomer. It is left in this at room-temperature until the peroxide has had time to penetrate the tissue before active polymerization begins. Since the peroxide was damped, it is necessary once more to dry the methacrylate

G

with anhydrous sodium sulphate. The temperature is then increased to about 50° C and the hardening starts.

Each molecule of benzoyl peroxide loses two of carbon dioxide, and two phenyl radicles are set free. Each phenyl radicle reacts with a monomer molecule, forming a covalent bond with

the carbon of the $\overset{H}{\underset{H}{C=}}$ group. The compound necessarily has an

uneven number of electrons, but the odd electron now appears

$$H_5C_6-\overset{H}{\underset{H}{C}}-\overset{CH_3}{\underset{\underset{O(CH_2)_3CH_3}{C}}{\overset{\displaystyle\cdot}{C}}}$$

A phenyl radicle combined with butyl methacrylate
Note the unpaired electron.

in a new place, at the other end of the methacrylate. Meanwhile the double bond has become single. The end of the molecule provided with the odd electron has become as active as the phenyl radicle was, and in exactly the same way. It combines with another monomer, and an unpaired electron is thus produced at the extremity of the latter. So the process goes on, and a high polymer is built up. The whole of it consists of methacrylate monomers, except one extremity of the chain.

This process of polymerization leads to the production of very long molecules, but it does not continue indefinitely. The growing end of the chain may come up against another growing end, or against a free radicle; in either case combination occurs, and the chain becomes 'dead'.

The process that has been described would lead only to the formation of molecules having the form of long, thin threads. In fact, however, branching and net-formation occur. Branching takes place in various ways in addition-polymers,[70] but the following is probably what happens in methacrylates.[158] A carbon atom, other than a terminal one, becomes active. The atom is thought to be one of those in the butyl group. This carbon atom lets go of one of its hydrogens, which departs with its single electron and attaches itself to the growing point of another molecule (which is thus terminated and becomes 'dead'). The carbon atom now has an uneven number of electrons, and therefore acts as a new growing point, to which other monomers add themselves one after another. The branch thus formed may

$$
\begin{array}{c}
\text{CH}_3 \\
\text{H} \mid \\
-\text{C}-\text{C}- \\
\text{H} \mid \text{O} \\
\text{C}\diagdown\text{H} \\
\diagdown \text{OC(CH}_2)_2\text{CH}_3
\end{array}
$$

A segmer of butyl methacrylate, with an active carbon (C) in the butyl radicle

itself be terminated and 'die' as a loose end; but if it meets another growing branch, the two may fuse and thus accomplish a union between two branched molecules that were previously separate. Since the branches are not all formed in the same plane, a three-dimensional meshwork results.

Tissues shrink slightly in butyl methacrylate while the latter is still in monomeric form.[9] Polymerization involves further shrinkage, since the methacrylate itself becomes reduced in volume. The various methacrylate esters differ from one another in this respect. The longer the molecule of the esterifying alcohol, the less the reduction in volume on polymerizing. Butyl methacrylate contracts to about 85% of its former volume, methyl methacrylate to about 79%.[158] The butyl ester is therefore preferable unless a very hard block is required. Measurements of the volume of the embedded tissue[9] suggest that this shrinks more than the methacrylate. Shrinkage is less than with paraffin, and since it is nearly equal in all directions, there is scarcely any distortion.

Blocks containing tissue can be stored indefinitely in the dry condition. To obtain sections from 8 μ to 1 μ thick, it is best to soak the block overnight in 70% ethanol and to cut on a sliding microtome with an oblique knife flooded with 70% ethanol.[26] The back of the knife should be raised rather higher above the level of the cutting edge than is usual when cutting paraffin. Sections may be stored in 70% ethanol.

Thin sections for electron microscopy are usually cut with knives made by breaking a piece of plate glass along a line at an angle of 45° to one of its edges.[107] The cutting edge is the one at the intersection of the two surfaces that subtend an angle of 45° to each other.

Methacrylate sections may be stuck to glass slides for study by phase-contrast microscopy (p. 128) in the same way as paraffin sections.[26] They are brought from 70% ethanol to water, and floated on very dilute albumen solution on a glass slide. To remove the embedding medium after the section has been attached, it is only necessary to put the slide in ethyl acetate or toluene, which dissolves the polymer. The slide is then passed through the usual series of ethanols to distilled water, and mounted in diluted glycerol (p. 128).

CHAPTER 7

Introduction to the Chemical Composition of Dyes

It is best to give the general name of 'colouring agents' or 'colorants' to substances used in microtechnique to colour or blacken the parts of organisms.

Colouring agents are used in very diverse ways. It is a strange fact that the housewife is more careful in her terminology of colouring agents than many microscopists are. She distinguishes clearly between *staining* and *painting* the floor, while they often use the word 'staining' without regard for the diversity of the processes grouped by them under this single name. The 'staining' of specimens by electron-microscopists has no connexion with dyeing. The word was formerly used as a synonym for 'dyeing', but has come to be treated so loosely in microtechnique that it is avoided in this book.

There are five principal ways of using colouring agents to distinguish the microscopical parts of organisms. In this book we are primarily concerned with only one of these, namely, *dyeing*; but this one is best understood by contrast with the others. The five will be briefly described here.

Injection of suspended coloured particles into closed spaces. We may suspend minute, insoluble, coloured particles in a fluid and inject this into the blood-vessels or other internal spaces of an organism. The final distribution of the coloured particles will be determined by their incapacity to penetrate the walls of the vessels into which the fluid has been forced. The chemical nature of the colouring agent is irrelevant, provided that it is insoluble.

Uptake of suspended coloured particles by phagocytic cells. We may provide a phagocytic cell with minute coloured particles suspended in the fluid in which it lives, and allow it to eat them. The distribution of the coloured particles at any time will be determined by the vital activity of the cell (movements of the cytoplasm, &c.). The particles will not colour any pre-existent object in the cell.

Solution of a lysochrome. We may dissolve a lipid-soluble colouring agent (not a dye) in 70% ethanol or some other suitable medium, and soak a section of fixed tissue in it. The lipids of the tissue will take up the colouring agent simply because it is more soluble in them than in 70% ethanol, and the distribution of the colour will be determined by this. Such colouring agents are called lysochromes, because they colour by solution (Greek *lúsis*, solution).[21]

Local formation of a coloured substance. We may soak the fixed tissues in a solution of a substance that will react with one or more of the tissue-constituents to produce an indiffusible coloured product; the solution used will be colourless or differently coloured from the product. Thus a yellow solution of potassium ferrocyanide will give a blue precipitate of insoluble Prussian blue wherever there is ferric iron in the tissue. The distribution of the colour will depend on the chemical properties of the reactive substance or substances in the tissue. Many histochemical tests fall into this category of colouring reactions.

Dyeing. We may soak tissues (living or dead) in a solution of a dye. Certain tissue-constituents will combine with the coloured ions of the dye and thus become coloured. The colour will usually not change. The final distribution of the dye will depend on the ability of the dye to penetrate the tissues and on the affinity of the tissue-constituents for its coloured ions.

The nature of dyeing is only briefly indicated by what has just been said, but it will be clear that the process is entirely different from the first three described above. It shows some resemblance to the fourth, but there are important differences. Dyes do not usually change colour when their ions are taken up by the tissues; and the uptake is generally far less specific, for most parts of the cell are capable of being dyed to some extent by most dyes, if sufficient time is allowed.

For the purposes of microtechnique, dyes may be defined thus. They are aromatic, salt-like, crystalline solids, that dissolve in water or aqueous solutions in the form of ions; either the cations or the anions (occasionally both) are coloured; the coloured ions can link themselves chemically with proteins (and generally with other tissue-constituents as well); when the linkage takes place, the ions do not lose colour, and usually they do not change it.

Two questions present themselves. What causes dyes to be coloured, and what causes their coloured ions to attach themselves to tissue-constituents? The first question will be considered here, the second in chapter 8.

Many of the familiar colours of nature—the brilliant wings of many butterflies, for instance, and the iridescent feathers of birds—owe their colour to parallel plates or parallel striations, separated by distances varying from about a quarter of a wavelength to a few wave-lengths of visible light. These 'structural' colours disappear when the substance is dissolved, because they are not due to any colour intrinsic in the molecules or lesser particles of the substance. It is only when such particles themselves show a differential transmission of light of different wavelengths, that a substance remains coloured on solution.

If all substances that remain coloured on solution are examined, it is found that most of them fall into a few major groups. It is a familiar fact that the salts of chromium, iron, and cobalt are coloured, and that colour is retained when they are dissolved. These are only examples of the wide generalization that the ions and ionic complexes formed by the transition elements are coloured; or, to dig a little more deeply into causes, we may say that the elements that give coloured ions are those metals that possess an incomplete shell of electrons inside their outermost shell. That is to say, the cause lies in intra-atomic structure. No dye, however, owes its colour to the possession of a transition element, nor indeed to the possession of any particular atom as such: its colour is due to its inter-atomic, not its intra-atomic structure.

Many aromatic, but few aliphatic compounds are coloured; and this suggests that there must be something in ring-structure that favours the production of colour: that is to say, that favours the absorption of light of particular wave-lengths. This is true; and all dyes are aromatic compounds. Benzene itself, the simplest of this group of substances, would appear coloured if we could see a short way into the ultra-violet, for it has an absorption-band at the wave-length of 256 mμ. The molecule may be thought

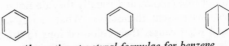

Alternative structural formulae for benzene

of as 'resonating' between different molecular configurations; that is, undergoing rapid change from one to another.

The alternation of single and double bonds between carbon atoms is favourable to resonance and the associated absorption of electro-magnetic waves; but there are certain molecular arrangements that excite the molecule to a particular degree, so

The paraquinonoid   *Parabenzoquinone*
ring

that light of greater wave-length is affected, and colour results. A very frequent arrangement of this sort in dyes is the quinonoid. All substances possessing a paraquinonoid ring are coloured.

Parabenzoquinone is the simplest of such substances. It is a pale yellow solid, dissolving in water to give a pale yellow solution, but it is not a dye. It dissolves to form a solution of molecules, whereas dyes dissolve as ions. Parabenzoquinone has no special tendency to attach itself to proteins or other tissue-constituents in such a way as to impart colour to them: dyes have such a tendency, powerfully developed.

The structure of dyes may be illustrated by the one known commercially as *pararosaniline*. (The *para* in this word is not used in its chemical sense.) This is a magenta solid, easily soluble in water. To make it, one needs aniline and paratoluidine. Aniline

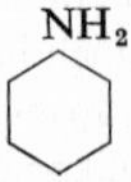

NH$_2$ NH$_2$

Aniline 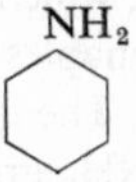   *Aniline*

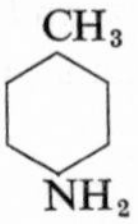

CH$_3$

NH$_2$

Paratoluidine

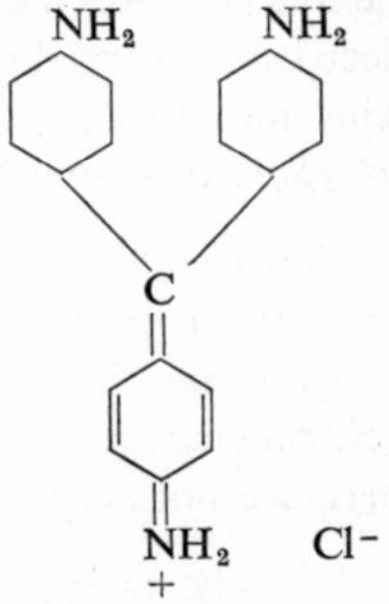

NH$_2$ NH$_2$

C

NH$_2$ Cl$^-$
+

Pararosaniline

is a colourless fluid (if pure), paratoluidine a colourless, crystalline solid. Heat them in the presence of a mild oxidizing agent and a source of chloride ions, and a brilliant colour develops. Two molecules of aniline combine with one of paratoluidine to give a substance in which one of the three rings is *quinonoid*.

To which of the three rings is colour due: to those derived from aniline, or to that derived from paratoluidine? The formula

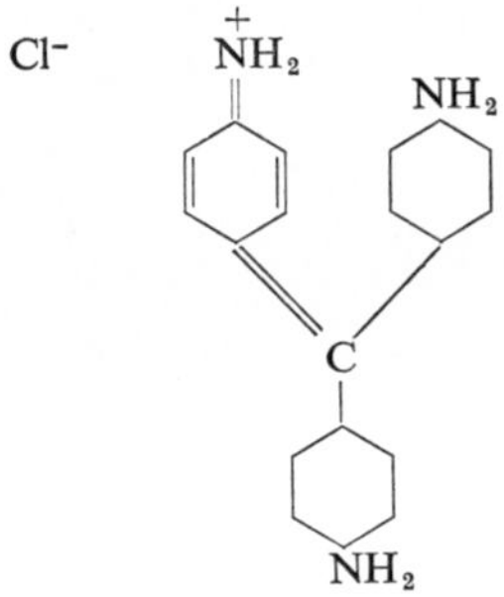

Cl$^-$ $\overset{+}{\text{N}}$H$_2$

NH$_2$

C

NH$_2$

*Pararosaniline: another
resonance position*

given first suggests the latter, but other formulae show the structure equally well. In fact, there is resonance between different structures: one may think of the positive electric charge as being now in one position, now in another.

The dye possesses a quinonoid ring, which gives it colour, and an electrically charged group, which enables it to attach itself to proteins and other tissue-constituents. The quinonoid ring is the *chromophore* or colour-bearer; the $-NH_2$ groups, all capable of conversion to $=\overset{+}{N}H_2$, are the auxochromes or colour-helpers, which help the chromophore to attach itself, and often greatly increase the intensity of the colours. The substance as a whole has the general character of a salt.

There are not very many different auxochromes. Many dyes have the same auxochrome as pararosaniline, namely $=\overset{+}{N}H_2$. Since this group of atoms is positively charged, the coloured ion is the cation and the dye is called *cationic* or *basic*. The anion may be chloride or sulphate or acetate; any inorganic anion will do, provided that it gives sufficient solubility. Such dyes may be represented by the formula R^+Cl^-, if the anion is chloride. The hydrogens of the $=\overset{+}{N}H_2$ group are often substituted by methyl or ethyl, or by aryl (the latter being a benzene ring with one or more substitutions of hydrogen atoms).

In many dyes it is the negatively charged ion that is coloured; these dyes with coloured anions are called *anionic* or *acid*. Their cation is usually sodium or potassium. If it is sodium we may write the formula Na^+R^-; R^- means the coloured anion. Various auxochromes give the necessary negative charge. The most usual are the sulphonic, hydroxyl, and carboxyl groups, which ionize to give $-SO_3^-$, $-O^-$, and $-COO^-$ respectively.

It is to be noticed that the so-called 'acid' dyes are seldom acids. The possession of the potentially acidic groups (sulphonic, hydroxyl, and carboxyl) gave rise to the name. Such groups are called acid radicles, despite the fact that they can only form part of an acid if the cation is hydrogen. In a few dyes this is so; the simplest formula for such dyes is H^+R^-.

Beyond auxochromes and chromophores, dyes often possess atoms or groups of atoms that are called *modifiers*. Thus rosani-

Rosaniline

line differs from pararosaniline only in the possession of a single methyl group; this modifies the colour, making it very slightly bluer. (Basic fuchsine is a mixture of these two closely related dyes.) The methyl group is here a modifier. It has been mentioned that the hydrogens of basic auxochromes may also be replaced by methyl or ethyl or aryl groups; this again modifies the colour. Each replacement of one of these hydrogens in pararosaniline by methyl makes a bluer dye, and crystal violet, in which all six are replaced, is nearly blue. Ethyl and particularly aryl groups have even more blueing effect, and purely blue dyes such as methyl blue (p. 94) may be obtained in this way.

Dyes are classified into groups by their chromophores. Most of these groups contain both cationic and anionic dyes, possessing the auxochromes mentioned above; many of them in all groups have modifiers (frequently methyl or ethyl). The great majority of the dyes used in microtechnique owe their colour either to the quinonoid ring or to the azo-group, $-N{=}N-$ (p. 96). The quinonoid dyes, however, are so diverse that it is necessary to divide them into sub-groups, each characterized by a particular chromophore that can be represented in a skeleton formula. The principles of dyeing in microtechnique can be explained by the use of only a few dyes, belonging to a small number of groups.

We shall concern ourselves with only five sub-groups of quin-onoid dyes. All the dyes mentioned in this book are listed here for convenient reference, under the names of their groups and sub-groups.

Dyes are not known by their full chemical names, because these would be inconveniently long. Shorter names are used, many of which are to some extent descriptive. Initial letters, written in capitals, often form part of a name; these serve to distinguish a dye from others that are closely related. Thus SS means spirit-soluble (soluble in ethanol, not in water); G means *gelb* (yellow). The B of azure B is an arbitrary mark of distinction from two closely related dyes called azures A and C.

QUINONOID DYES

Triarylmethane
　　Cationic. Pararosaniline, rosaniline, methyl violet, crystal violet, aniline blue SS
　　Anionic. Methyl blue

Haematein
　　Anionic. Haematein

Anthraquinonoid
　　Anionic. Alizarine, purpurine, carminic acid

Xanthene
　　Anionic. Eosin

Thiazine
　　Cationic. Thionine, azure B

AZO DYES

Mono-azo
　　Anionic. Orange G

QUINONOID DYES

Triarylmethane dyes. These may be regarded as derived from leuco-pararosaniline, which is a colourless substance, since it possesses no chromophore. Leuco-pararosaniline itself is methane in which three of the four hydrogens have been replaced by aniline.

The aniline rings are merely particular examples of aryl rings, and

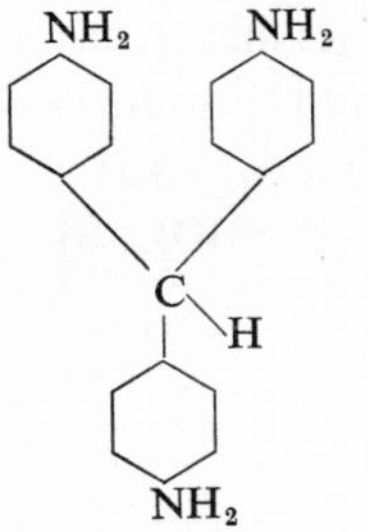

Leuco-para-
rosaniline

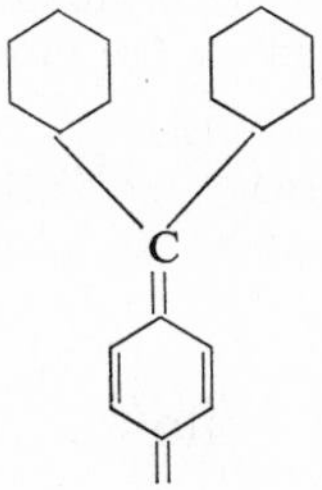

Skeleton-formula for
triarylmethane dyes

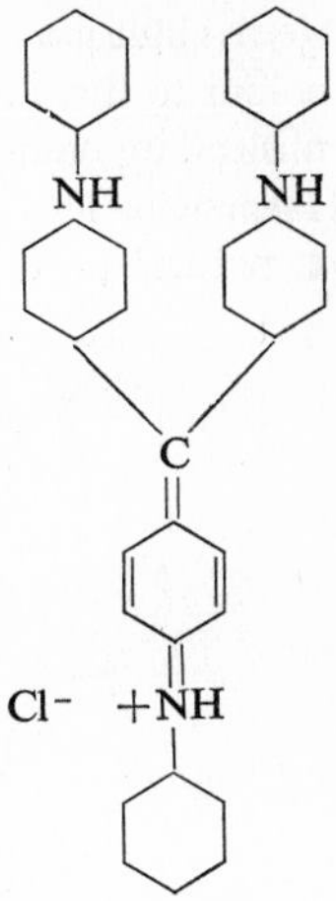

Triphenylpara-
rosaniline

all the many dyes that have three such rings held together in the same way, whether any of the rings has an $=\overset{+}{N}H_2$ group on it or not, are therefore classified together as triarylmethane dyes. In the skeleton-formula for this and other groups of dyes, the auxochromes and modifiers are omitted, since these differ from dye to dye.

Methyl violet is pararosaniline in which four or five of the hydrogens of the amino-groups have been replaced by methyl. This replacement has a strong blueing effect. When all six are replaced, crystal violet is produced; this dye is almost blue. It has already been mentioned (p. 91) that ethyl and aryl groups have still greater blueing effect than methyl. This is well exemplified by triphenyl pararosaniline, which, with another closely related dye, constitutes the mixture known as aniline blue SS. Triphenyl pararosaniline is a pure blue cationic dye. It is pararosaniline in which one of the hydrogens of each of the three amino-groups has been replaced by a phenyl group (that is, by a simple, unsubstituted aryl group).

Methyl blue is a pure blue anionic triarylmethane dye that owes its colour to three extra aryl groups acting as modifiers. Despite its misleading name, it possesses no methyl group.

Haematein. This is a very small group of dyes that are derived from natural products and are not made synthetically. As the

Skeleton-formula for   *Haematein*   *Catechol*
haematein dyes

formula shows, this is not only an acid dye, but actually an acid, related to catechol. It is of a brownish-red colour, but becomes blue in alkaline solution. It is therefore used as an indicator of pH, but it is not valuable by itself as a dye. When used with an intermediary or 'mordant' (p. 110) between itself and the tissues, it becomes one of the most important dyes used in microtechnique.

Haematein is derived from the heart-wood of a small leguminous tree, *Haematoxylon campechianum*, native to Central America. This contains a non-quinonoid substance, haematoxylin, which is not a dye and is indeed colourless, since it lacks a chromophore; but it is readily oxidized to haematein by weak oxidizing agents, including atmospheric oxygen. Haematoxylin is often sold in a partially oxidized form, as a brown powder that is really a mixture of haematoxylin and haematein.

Anthraquinonoid dyes. These are related to anthraquinone, a yellow, crystalline substance. The simplest is alizarine, the chief coloured constituent of madder, a vegetable dye. Alizarine is easily synthesized from anthraquinone. It is not used in microtechnique. Its more complex relative, carminic acid, is a parti-

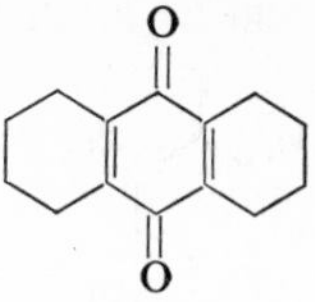

Anthraquinone

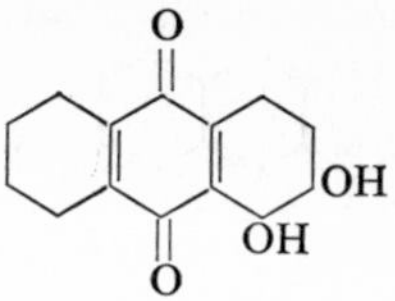

Alizarine

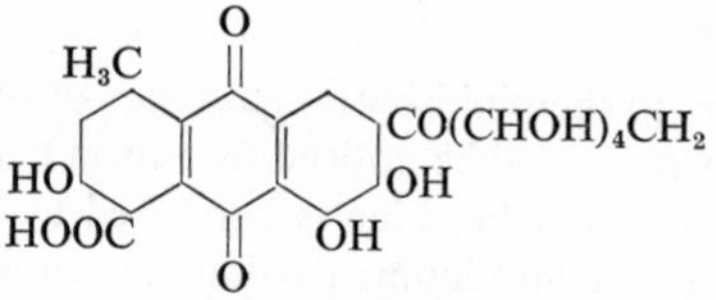

Carminic acid

cularly valuable dye in biological work. Carminic acid is soluble (unlike alizarine) in distilled water, and also in ethanol. It occurs naturally in the fat-body of the wingless females of the coccid *Dactylopius cacti*. This is a scale-insect that sucks the juices of the succulent plant *Nopalea coccinellifera*. The latter is cultivated in various subtropical parts of the world to provide the insect with food. The dried females constitute cochineal. Carmine is a crude form of the dye, produced by precipitating an aqueous extract of cochineal with alum (potassium aluminium sulphate). It is composed mainly of carminic acid bound to aluminium and to protein derived from the insect. Carmine is insoluble in distilled water; but solutions can be obtained (e.g. by the addition of acid or alkali), and the crude dye is usable in microtechnique. It is best to use the pure acid whenever one wants to know exactly what reactions are occurring.

One of the main uses of carmine in microtechnique is explained in the chapter on the use of mordants (p. 122).

Xanthene dyes. In these dyes, carbon and oxygen form links between two rings. Not many members of this group are commonly used in microtechnique. Eosin, however, is particularly familiar. It is a valuable 'background' dye: that is to say, it is anionic, pale, diffuse in action, and used to give contrast with objects picked out vividly in another colour by another dye.

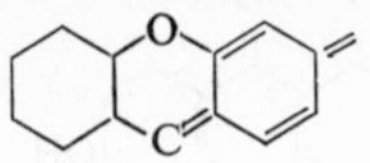

Skeleton-formula for
xanthene dyes

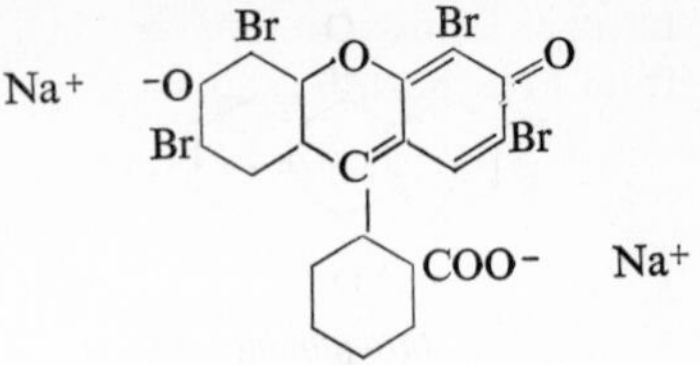

Eosin Y

The name refers to the pinkish-orange colour of the sky at dawn (Greek *ēōs*, dawn). It will be noticed that eosin has two different auxochromes, and that bromine is here used as a modifier. In related dyes chlorine and iodine partially or wholly replace the bromine, and a bluish tinge is thus imparted.

Thiazine dyes. Here sulphur and nitrogen link two rings (Greek *theion*, sulphur; French *azote*, nitrogen; the *a* in thiazine is short, as in *azote*). Thionine, a blue dye with a reddish tinge, is the

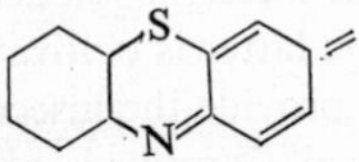

Skeleton-formula for
thiazine dyes

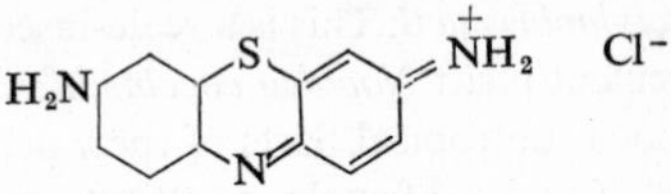

Thionine

simplest member of the group. The thiazines used in micro-technique are all cationic. They are valuable dyes for nucleo-proteins. Several of them, including thionine, are 'metachro-matic'; that is to say, they impart quite different colours to different substances (p. 104). This is a most valuable property, since it gives important indications of chemical composition. Azure B is another metachromatic thiazine dye. It is trimethyl thionine; that is to say, thionine modified by the substitution of three methyls for three of the four hydrogens of the amino-groups.

AZO DYES

These contain no quinonoid ring, apart from a few that have both azo and quinonoid chromophores. The name refers to the nitrogen atoms that link two rings together. (The name is derived from French *azote*; short *a*.)

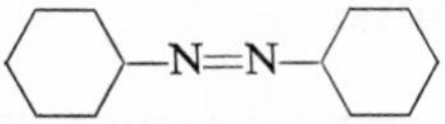

Skeleton-formula for
azo dyes

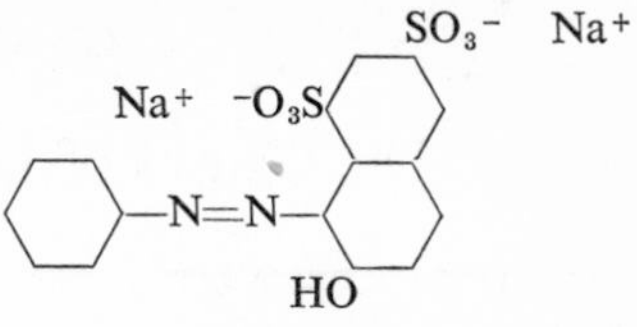

Orange G

The –N=N– group occurs once, twice, or thrice in the ion, which may be a cation or an anion; the corresponding group-names are mono-azo, disazo, and trisazo. The formula shows that orange G is an anionic, mono-azo dye; there are two –SO₃⁻ groups. The name refers to the colour, which is a very yellowish orange. This is a typical background dye.

Not all azo substances are dyes. Sudan IV, for example, possesses the azo chromophore and is coloured (red). The formula shows, however, that it lacks an auxochrome. It is in-

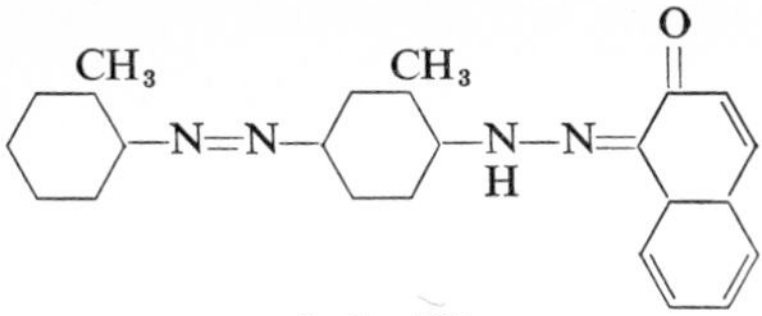

Sudan IV

soluble in water, but very soluble in lipids. It is an important lysochrome, used in histochemistry for the recognition of lipids. It is presented to the tissues at saturation in 70% ethanol. Being much more soluble in lipids than in this solvent, it accumulates in lipid globules and colours them. As we shall see in the next chapter, dyeing is a very different process from mere colouring by solution.

H

CHAPTER 8

The Causes of Differential Dyeing

When a section is soaked in a solution of a single dye, the various tissue-constituents react differently. There is differential uptake, and the varying intensity of coloration serves to distinguish the constituents. The latter may also react differently to different dyes, for a particular object may take up much of one, little of another. These facts make it possible to produce striking colour contrasts in what had been a transparent, colourless object. That, indeed, is the purpose of dyeing. We are now concerned with the causes that produce these effects.

Whether a particular object in a microscopical section is strongly or weakly coloured by a particular dye depends on three factors: the *chemical affinity* between the object and the dye, the *density* of the object, and the *permeability* of the object by the dye.

Chemical affinity

Some of the constituents of the tissues, in the form in which they appear on the slide in sections, are acidic. Examples are DNA and chromatin, RNA and ribonucleoprotein, the matrix of cartilage, the mucous secretions of certain gland-cells, and certain conjugated lipids. Other constituents, such as the ground-cytoplasm of most cells and the contractile substance of muscle, are neither particularly acidic nor particularly basic. They are markedly amphoteric; that is to say, their electric charge varies easily with the pH of the fluid in which they lie. Others again, such as collagen, the cytoplasm of red blood-corpuscles, and the granules of eosinophil leucocytes, are basic.

DNA, RNA, and phospholipids owe their acidity to their

98

phosphoric groups. The acidity of the mucopolysaccharides of cartilage and of certain mucous secretions is due to sulphuric and carboxyl groups. The amphoteric proteins owe their character to a balance between acidic amino-acids (aspartic, glutamic, hydroxyglutamic, &c.) and basic ones (lysine, arginine, and

$$
\begin{array}{l}
\quad | \\
\mathrm{NH} \\
\quad | \\
\mathrm{H\overset{|}{C}(CH_2)_2COOH} \quad \textit{glutamic acid} \\
\quad | \\
\mathrm{C{=}O} \\
\quad | \\
\mathrm{NH} \\
\quad | \\
\mathrm{H\overset{|}{C}(CH_2)_4NH_2} \quad \textit{lysine} \\
\quad | \\
\mathrm{C{=}O} \\
\quad |
\end{array}
$$

Part of a protein chain at the iso-electric point

histidine). The latter predominate in the basic proteins of collagen and red blood-corpuscles.

When a protein is put in a fluid at a pH below its iso-electric point, the amino-groups of its basic amino-acids tend to become positively charged as $-\overset{+}{N}H_3$. When the pH is above the iso-electric point, the carboxyl groups of the acidic amino-acids become ionized as $-COO^-$. If the proportions of basic and acidic amino-acids in a particular protein are about equal, the electric charge of the protein as a whole is easily shifted by variation in pH within the range of the fluids ordinarily used in microtechnique; but in fact all proteins can be shown to be amphoteric if there is a sufficient change of pH.

We have seen in chapter 7 that all dyes dissolve as ions, and that the coloured ions of some are positively charged, of others negatively. This can easily be proved by experiment. An agar gel is allowed to set in a vertical U-tube, and the dye-solution to be tested is added to both limbs of the tube, above the agar. The agar serves the mechanical function of holding the water in the U-tube nearly still. Salt must be dissolved with the agar, to permit the easy passage of an electric current. An electrode is placed in the dye-solution on each side. It is necessary to take the usual steps to prevent polarization of the electrodes; full practical instructions for setting up the apparatus have been given elsewhere.[21] When the current is switched on, the coloured ions begin to move down one or the other limb of the U-tube, towards either the cathode or the anode. The distance travelled in a given time depends on the concentration of the dye and of the agar, on the diffusibility of the dye, and on the strength of the electric current. In the apparatus referred to,[21] a movement of 2 or 3 cm in 24 hours is usual. There is often a much smaller movement of the coloured ions down the other limb of the U-tube. This is due to simple diffusion.

Most dyes can be described unequivocally as cationic (= basic) or anionic (= acid). Some, however, are amphoteric. Haematein is an example. This dye is cationic below pH 6·6 (the iso-electric point) but anionic above.

In general, the acidic (negatively charged) objects in tissues attract the cationic dyes, while the basic (positively charged) objects attract the anionic dyes. Since the former objects are easily dyed by basic dyes, they are called basiphil; the latter, since they are easily dyed by acid dyes, are called acidophil. It is to be remembered that basiphil objects are acidic, acidophil objects basic. Thus the nucleic acids, most nucleoproteins (ordinary 'chromatin', for instance), the matrix of cartilage, many mucous secretions, and certain conjugated lipids are basiphil; while collagen, the cytoplasm of red blood-corpuscles, and the granules of eosinophil leucocytes are acidophil.

It is useful to form a concrete idea of the effects of cationic and anionic dyes by studying sections of specially selected tissues. The testis, intestine, and pancreas of the mouse are suitable. Most fixatives leave the tissues in a state in which cationic dyes act well, but some are unfavourable to anionic ones. It is well to use Zenker's fluid for the present purpose, because it is especially favourable to the action of anionic dyes. Sections should be lightly dyed and then run quickly through the alcohols and xylene into a resinous mounting medium.

In sections coloured by cationic dyes, the most prominent

feature is the strong colouring of chromatin. Metaphase and anaphase chromosomes, both mitotic and meiotic, are more deeply coloured than anything else; nuclei are conspicuous on account of their chromatin content. The mucous secretion of the goblet-cells in the intestine may be rather strongly dyed, frequently in a different colour from anything else (p. 105). The cytoplasm of most kinds of cells (such as spermatogonia and spermatocytes, and the interstitial cells of the testis) is scarcely tinged. Certain kinds of cells, however, have a large amount of ribonucleic acid in the cytoplasm, and this takes the dye. The epithelial cells of the crypts of Lieberkühn are examples; the bases of the exocrine cells of the pancreas are even more strongly dyed, because of the particularly great amount of ribonucleic acid associated with the massive endoplasmic reticulum of this region. There is scarcely any colour, however, in the contractile substance of smooth muscle, in collagen fibres, in the free border of the intestinal epithelium, or in the large granules of the Paneth cells in the crypts of Lieberkühn. There is nothing to distinguish the granules of the eosinophil leucocytes in the cores of the intestinal villi, and these cells can scarcely be recognized. Red blood-corpuscles are not dyed.

The whole aspect of sections of the same tissues coloured with a typical anionic dye is entirely different. There is a general colouring of the cytoplasm of most kinds of cells. The cytoplasm of the interstitial cells of the testis takes up more of the dye than that of the spermatogenetic cells, and groups of the former kind of cells therefore stand out rather prominently under the low power of the microscope. The basal part of the exocrine cells of the pancreas is moderately deeply coloured. The cytoplasm of the epithelium of the crypts is pale. The contractile substance of smooth muscle takes the dye; so do collagen fibres. None of these tissue-constituents, however, is nearly so strongly coloured as certain cytoplasmic granules, namely those of the Paneth cells and particularly the minute ones of the eosinophil leucocytes in the cores of the villi. Chromatin shows no special affinity for the dye and is only lightly coloured. The nuclear sap is colourless. The nuclei therefore often appear almost as though they were

cavities in the dyed cytoplasm, and they are not nearly so conspicuous as in sections coloured with a cationic dye. Red blood-
corpuscles will take any anionic dye that is able to enter them
(p. 108).

It must not be supposed that basiphil objects are necessarily
resistant to coloration by anionic dyes, or acidophil ones to
coloration by cationic dyes. Proteins that are predominantly
acidic contain some basic amino-acids, and conversely. Thus all
the proteins in a cell can eventually be dyed to some extent by any
dye, whether basic or acid. However, by controlling the times
during which the dyes act, it is easy to ensure that the basiphil
objects will be dyed by cationic (basic) dyes and the acidophil
ones by anionic (acid) dyes, each almost to the exclusion of the
other.

The amphoteric objects in cells can be dyed with either cationic
or anionic dyes, by controlling the pH. In practice one usually
wants to leave the cytoplasm uncoloured, or else to dye it differently from the chromatin. If a cationic dye is used in slightly
acid solution (methyl green, for instance, in a weak solution of
acetic acid), the chromatin will be coloured: but the amphoteric
cytoplasm, having been rendered basic by the acidity of the
solution, will have very little affinity for the cationic dye, and the
cytoplasm will therefore appear colourless or nearly so. Alternatively one may use a cationic dye in acid solution first, and then
an anionic one of contrasting colour. The amphoteric cytoplasm
will have some affinity for the anionic dye, and it can thus be
coloured differentially.

Since most tissue-constituents will eventually be coloured to
some extent by any dye, it may be desirable to limit the period of
dyeing, so that some of them will appear colourless when others
have already been quite strongly dyed. In other words, dyeing
may be arrested at a particular stage instead of being allowed to
go to completion. This is *progressive* dyeing, so called because the
depth of colour becomes progressively greater until the desired
end is reached. In *regressive* dyeing, on the contrary, the tissues
are allowed to take up an excess of the dye, and the latter is then
partly removed, with careful control under the microscope, until

certain tissue-constituents have lost the colour while others retain it. During this regressive process the parts become more distinct from one another than they were when all parts held too much of the dye. The regressive stage of the process is therefore called *differentiation*.

Cationic dyes are frequently used regressively. It is customary to use acids as differentiating agents. They act, in principle, in exactly the same way as when they are mixed with the dye: reliance is placed on the ability of the acid to render the amphoteric tissue-constituents basic, and thus make them let go of the cationic (basic) dye. Alkalis can be used in the same way to differentiate acid dyes.

An alternative way of differentiating is to soak the tissue in a fluid in which the tendency of the dye to remain ionized is reduced or eliminated, but in which the dye is soluble. Ethanol, either absolute or in strong aqueous solution, is often used for this purpose. The dye is rapidly lost from those tissue-constituents that hold little of it. If differentiation be stopped as soon as these constituents appear colourless, the objects that still retain a considerable amount of the dye will contrast strongly with them. The tissue must now be brought quickly into a fluid, such as xylene, in which the dye is insoluble.

Acidic tissue-constituents, lacking any basic groups, can in certain circumstances be dyed by anionic (acid) dyes. Thus methyl blue, an anionic triarylmethane dye, will colour cellulose cell-walls. Indeed, it is used in the textile industry for dyeing cotton, and is often called cotton blue. The structural formula for cellulose shows the absence of any group that would be

Part of a cellulose molecule

thought likely to attract an acid dye. It is supposed that the linkage is through a hydrogen bond,[73] for it will be remembered that hydrogen can in certain circumstances act as though it were bivalent. Such a bond may tie the hydrogen of a hydroxyl group of cellulose to the nitrogen of an amino-group (or substituted amino-group) in a dye. Now methyl blue, and certain other anionic triarylmethane dyes that will colour cellulose, do contain nitrogen in a substituted amino-group.

The hydrogens of the peptide groups of nylon are thought to form hydrogen bonds with the amino-groups of certain dyes in much the same way. If so, it is likely that the peptide groups of

$$\begin{array}{c} | \\ C{=}O \\ | \\ NH \\ | \end{array}$$

Peptide group in nylon or protein

protein could behave similarly. This may account for the tendency of certain acid dyes to colour tissue-constituents without appearing to discriminate between those that are positively and negatively charged.

It is thought by some that dyes are first brought close to particular tissue-constituents by the interaction of electrical charges, and are then tied closely to them by 'short-range' forces; that is to say, by covalent or hydrogen bonds.[134] Whether a close tying-up of this sort does or does not occur finally as a general rule in microtechnical dyeing, the distribution of dyes is in the main determined by the electrical charges, density, and permeability of the tissue-constituents.

It has already been remarked (p. 86) that dye-ions are usually taken up without change of colour. An important exception to this rule must now be briefly mentioned.

Certain pure (unmixed) dyes have the property of dyeing particular tissue-constituents in a colour that differs from that of the solution. This is called *metachromasy* and the dye is called *metachromatic*; the tissue-constituents that are dyed in a differing colour are called *chromotropes* (colour-turners).

All the metachromatic dyes that are commonly used in micro-technique are basic, and they all act on the same chromotropes. The metachromasy of acid dyes will not be considered in this book.

The metachromatic dyes do not form a chemical group by themselves. On the contrary, they are distributed among all the major groups except the azo. Methyl violet is a metachromatic triarylmethane dye, for instance; thionine and azure B are meta-chromatic thiazines. (Commercial thionine is often adulterated with a red dye, and may then give false metachromatic colours.[104]) It is a curious fact that when all the hydrogens of the amino-groups of a dye are replaced by methyl, the resulting substance is not metachromatic.[110] Thus crystal violet (p. 93) is not meta-chromatic (though in commerce it is often adulterated with the strongly metachromatic methyl violet).

The colour-shift caused by chromotropes is always in the same direction. Green dyes become bluish; blue dyes are reddened to purple or red; red ones become orange or yellow. This means that the absorption-maximum of the dye moves in all cases towards the shorter wave-lengths.

Chromotropes are necessarily acidic, since they have affinity for cationic dyes. Their negative charges are due to the possession of sulphuric, phosphoric, or carboxyl groups. Many of the most familiar chromotropes are sulphuric esters of polysaccharides of high molecular weight.[110] These are often mucosubstances. Thus the matrix of cartilage, the secretions of certain mucous glands, and the granules of the basiphil cells (*Mastzellen*) of connective tissue give metachromatic colours because they contain chon-droitic acid, mucoitic acid, and heparin respectively. Not all chromotropes, however, are mucosubstances. Agar, strongly chromotropic, lacks an amino-group.

The cause of metachromasy has not been established with certainty. The metachromatic dyes have a tendency to form dimers and polymers, of the metachromatic colour, in aqueous solution. Chromotropes appear to be substances that favour strongly the dimeric and polymeric forms of the dye, and hold the dye to themselves in its dimeric or particularly its polymeric form.[110, 125, 124, 178] A small molecule would not be able to hold a high polymer of a dye, but a polymeric substance, with numerous negative charges arranged on its surface at regular and convenient distances apart, might be able to do so.[178] It thus appears that the mode of attachment of the dye causes the shift of colour.

Metachromasy is important in cytological technique because it acts as a pointer towards chemical composition.

Density

Make two gelatine gels, one containing 5% and the other 20% of gelatine. Fix these in formaldehyde solution (or in a mixture containing formaldehyde). Cut a section of each on the freezing microtome, at the same thickness (say 15 μ). Allow an aqueous solution of any dye to act on both sections for the same period, which must be sufficient to allow complete permeation. Rinse with distilled water. It is not surprising that one section is more strongly coloured than the other. The result is due solely to the fact that one section is *denser* than the other: that is to say, it contains more colourable matter than the other, and therefore takes up more dye.

One often reads that the cytoplasm of a particular cell is 'dense'. How did the writer know? The depth of colouring may be due to quite different causes. If one had not made the gelatine gels oneself, one would not have known the cause of the difference in colouring. The density of the two sections might have been exactly the same, but one of them might have been made of a basic and the other of an acidic protein, and they would necessarily have taken up different amounts of any particular dye.

Anyone who performs the experiment just described is likely to be surprised by the darkness of the section that contains more gelatine. There is only four times as much gelatine, but it appears to have taken up much more than four times as much dye. This is, in fact, an illusion. Let us suppose that we have used a black dye, and that the section made from the weaker gelatine gel stops one-half of the light that is shone on to its surface. Make a pile of four such sections, one on top of the other, and illuminate them from below. The second from the bottom receives half the original light, and sends up half of what it receives to the next; this halves the light again, and so does the uppermost section. Thus only one-sixteenth of the light gets through. But in these four sections together there is the same amount of gelatine—and therefore the same amount of dye—as in a single section cut from the stronger gel. The latter, for the same reason, lets through only one-sixteenth of the incident light, though the amount of dye is only four times as great as in the section that let through one-half. For this reason we are apt to form an exaggerated opinion of the difference in the amount of dye taken up by objects in microscopical preparations.

When dividing cells are coloured with a cationic (basic) dye, each metaphase chromosome takes up far more of it than an equal volume of cytoplasm does. This results partly from the fact that nucleoprotein is much more acidic (basiphil) than the cytoplasm, but partly also from the fact that the chromosomes are denser. Their density is indicated by the fact that *anionic* (*acid*) dyes also colour chromosomes more deeply than the cytoplasm; indeed, they are used to colour chromatin in several familiar techniques. For instance, acid fuchsine is used for this purpose in Mallory's method for the differential colouring of collagen.[114] Whenever a particular object can be more deeply dyed than the cytoplasm or nuclear sap by both anionic and cationic dyes, it is likely to be denser (though one requires an interference microscope for the actual measurement of density). The converse, however, is not necessarily true: we cannot conclude that a particular object contains little matter, from the fact that it takes up little or no dye. It may possess few or no acidic or basic groups, capable of attachment to cationic or anionic dyes. Thus triglyceride droplets, though very dense, cannot be dyed.

Permeability

The amount of dye taken up by an object in a particular time does not depend solely on the amount of matter it contains, or on the abundance of charged groups. It depends also on whether the dye can permeate the object easily. Certain dyes have a great capacity for penetration, others very little.[64, 65, 130, 168] It is easy to test this capacity.[21] It is only necessary to allow some gelatine or agar to set into gels in test-tubes, and then to add solutions of different dyes, all at the same concentrations, to different tubes. Some dyes diffuse quickly into the gel, some slowly. Eosin (xanthene) and orange G (azo) are examples of rapidly permeating dyes, methyl blue (triarylmethane) of slowly permeating. In general, the rapidly permeating dissolve as single ions (and not very large ones); the slowly permeating tend to form colloidal solutions, in which each particle is an aggregate of several ions.

In microtechnique we make use of the varying rates of penetration to colour differentially objects that carry the same electric charge. Thus collagen and the red blood-corpuscles of vertebrates both contain a high proportion of basic protein and are therefore acidophil. It is quite easy, however, to colour them differently with two different anionic (acid) dyes. The mixture of methyl blue nnd eosin devised by the Oxford histologist, Mann, serves the purpose well.[115, 116] Methyl blue is much the more powerful dye (partly, perhaps, because a single positive charge in the object may be able to attract a whole ion-aggregate). Wherever the two dyes can compete, methyl blue predominates and the colour is blue or bluish. This applies to collagen fibres, which are evidently loose-textured, for they are easily coloured by aggregated dye-ions. Red blood-corpuscles, on the contrary, are very close-textured, and they are much more easily entered by separate dye-ions than by aggregates. The result is that Mann's methyl blue/eosin dyes collagen blue and red blood-corpuscles orange-red.

The various tissue-constituents can be arranged in the order of their permeability. Collagen is very permeable; cytoplasm less so; the contractile substance of muscle less so again; red blood-corpuscles are particularly impermeable. It is possible to dye collagen in one colour, cytoplasm and contractile substance in another, and red blood-corpuscles in a third, by the use of three different anionic dyes. The result is achieved without any reliance on different chemical affinities.

The three qualities in the tissue-constituents that make possible the differential action of dyes—chemical affinity, density, and permeability—may act together or may antagonize one another. Chromatin, for instance, is chemically reactive (basiphil), dense, but permeable: all these characters act together to render it easily coloured by cationic dyes. Red blood-corpuscles, on the contrary, are chemically reactive (acidophil), dense, but very impermeable. A microscopical preparation coloured with two or three dyes owes its variegated appearance to complex interactions, and it is not always easy to disentangle the effects of the three factors.

Those anionic dyes that penetrate readily tend to colour all acidophil and amphoteric tissue-constituents about equally deeply, and they are therefore diffuse in action. They are useful 'background' dyes, giving colour-contrast to a cationic dye used for chromatin. If methyl blue or a similar anionic dye were used instead of a diffuse one, it might spoil the effect by giving some of its colour to chromatin.

It is best to choose background dyes of colours near the middle of the visible spectrum (yellowish or green), since these appear to the human eye as 'unsaturated'; that is to say, they stimulate all the colour-receptors in the retina to some extent and thus appear pale, as though mixed with white. Orange G, being yellow, is suitable. For contrast the chromatin should be dyed in a 'saturated' colour near one end of the spectrum (red, blue, or violet). Violet gives the best contrast with yellow, because the colours are complementary.

If chromatin be dyed black or grey, any background dye will necessarily reduce the contrast.

CHAPTER 9

The Action of Mordants

Up till now we have been concerned with the direct attachment of dyes to tissue-constituents. In some of the most important processes of dyeing, however, an intermediary or *mordant* stands between the dye and the tissue. The dye attaches itself to the mordant: the latter (as its name suggests) 'eats into' or grips the tissue.

The great advantage of mordanting is that the colour is not removable by neutral fluids, whether aqueous or alcoholic. One may therefore colour progressively or regressively until the tissue is properly displayed, and then dehydrate at leisure, or counterstain as desired. The fact that dehydration may be done as slowly as one pleases is particularly helpful in making whole mounts. As we shall see, it is chiefly chromatin that is coloured by most mordant dyes. Nuclei are crowded together in the epithelial parts of many organs, but are sparse in the connective tissues; and there may be cavities from which they are absent. Thus the dyeing of chromatin gives clear micro-anatomical pictures in whole mounts, even with quite low powers of the microscope.

The fastness of mordant dyes makes them suitable for use in aqueous mounts, provided that acidity is avoided.

All dyes that act with mordants can also be used without them, but if so their effects are quite different. By no means all dyes can be used with mordants. The chief ones so used in microtechnique are carminic acid and haematein. The chief mordants used with them are salts of aluminium and of ferric iron.

In the textile industry the chief dyes used with mordants are azo dyes, and the chief mordants are complex basic salts of chromium. The chemistry of the mordanting of azo dyes by chromium has been carefully worked out by the textile chemists.[83, 155, 82, 36] Unfortunately it is radically different from the mordanting of carminic acid or haematein by aluminium or ferric salts.

One of the simplest dyes that can be mordanted is purpurine, which, like carminic acid, is an anthraquinone dye. Alizarine is even simpler, but its low solubility in suitable solvents makes it less convenient in practical use. The third –OH group, which

Alizarine   *Purpurine*

occurs in purpurine but not in alizarine, is rather unreactive, and the two dyes tend to behave similarly with mordants.[131] Both dyes occur naturally in the form of glucosides in the root of the madder plant, *Rubia tinctorum* (Rubiaceae), but the synthetic products are almost invariably used. Purpurine is unfortunately named, for it is a red dye.

If purpurine is dissolved at saturation in 60% ethanol, it acts as a typical though very weak acid dye. This can be shown by carrying out the tests described on p. 101. If, however, the dye is dissolved in a solution of aluminium sulphate, the result is entirely different. The following is a convenient solution.

Take 0·8 g of purpurine and 7·88 g of aluminium sulphate crystals $(16H_2O)$; add 450 ml of 60% ethanol; boil with reflux condenser until the solids have dissolved; cool; make up to 500 ml with 60% ethanol.[23]

The purpurine in this solution, if pure, is at $M/160$, the aluminium sulphate at $M/40$. The solution may be called standard aluminium purpurine, or 'purpural' for short.

The ethanol in this solution increases the solubility of the dye and thus makes the solution last longer when used repeatedly; it slows down or prevents the growth of bacteria and moulds; and it decreases ionization and thus 'equalizes' the action on tissues (that is to say, prevents the solution from over-dyeing locally).

Restrainers such as ethanol and glycerol are particularly useful in the dyeing of whole mounts, but they sometimes serve a useful purpose with sections also, especially when dyes are used progressively.

The various tissue-constituents mentioned on p. 101 are coloured by purpural exactly as though it were a basic dye (p. 90). There is, however, this difference, that whereas basic dyes can be washed out of the tissues by neutral alcoholic solutions (50% or 70% ethanol, for instance), mordanted purpurine cannot.

Other soluble salts of aluminium (the chloride, for instance) may be substituted for the sulphate: the action is again that of a basic dye. If, however, sodium sulphate is used instead of the aluminium salt, there is no mordanting and purpurine acts as a very weak acid dye. Thus it is the cation that mordants.

It will be remembered that metallic aluminium has three electrons in its outer 'shell' (the third or 'M' shell). In its salts these are lost to the anion, and the cation is left with the same orbital electrons as the inert gas neon. The cation has, however, the ability to accept electrons from suitable donor atoms, and in the presence of water it accepts no fewer than 12, two from each of 6 oxygens in water molecules. In solution the cation consists of aluminium in the centre, with 6 molecules of water surrounding it.[45, 173] The 6 dative covalency bonds are arranged in opposite pairs, each pair being at right-angles to the other two pairs. Each valency bond holds a molecule of water (fig. 6, left).

It may be wondered why exactly 6 bonds are formed, involving the donation by water of 12 electrons. This is controlled partly by the geometrical fact that 6 water molecules fit round a central atom or ion more easily than (say) 5 or 7, but there is also another cause. The reader may recall that the M shell will hold a total of 18 electrons, but these cannot all be accepted when the atomic nucleus is that of aluminium. Twelve have the faculty of 'hybridizing' with one another, without distinction as to whether they belong to the s, p, or d orbitals of the shell; and these 12 give the dative covalency of six.

The complex water/aluminium ion, having 3 electrons less than the total number required to neutralize the protons of its atomic

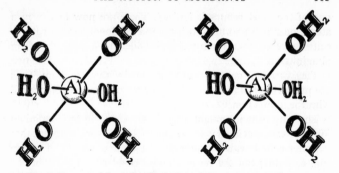

Fig. 6. Structural formulae for hydrated aluminium ions, drawn in perspective. The ion on the left carries three positive charges. That on the right has lost a hydrogen ion and carries two positive charges.

nuclei (aluminium, oxygen, and hydrogen, together), may be regarded as holding 3 positive charges at the moment of its formation. The 6 water molecules, however, do not all remain intact. One of them, at least, tends to lose a hydrogen ion,[45] which joins a molecule of the solvent water to form a hydronium ion, H_3O^+, and thus departs. Since it carries off a positive charge, the complex ion (fig. 6, right) is only doubly charged; but the solution, having gained a hydronium ion, has become acid. Thus the pH of an $M/40$ solution of aluminium sulphate in 60% ethanol is 3·08.

When purpurine is dissolved in water or in solutions of ethanol in water, it behaves like a phenol; that is to say, like a weak acid. A saturated solution in 60% ethanol has a pH of 5·20. Some of the hydrogens of the –OH groups are ionized and lost, and the dye is now negatively charged. In the structural formula shown here,

Ionized purpurine

The aluminium purpurine ion

one of the –OH groups is ionized. There are now two oxygen atoms near one another, both capable of donating electrons to suitable acceptors. If purpurine is added to a solution of an aluminium salt, these two oxygen atoms will tend to replace two of the water molecules that are combined with aluminium. Thus the purpurine will form a complex or 'co-ordination compound' with the aluminium.[172]

The purpurine ion might attach itself either to an aluminium ion that was associated with 6 water molecules, or else to one that was associated with 5 water molecules and one –OH group (fig. 6, right); but the resulting compound would probably be the same in both cases, for the acceptance of purpurine by the aluminium atom would be likely to be accompanied by the acceptance of a hydrogen ion from a hydronium ion in the solution, which would attach itself to the –OH group of the hydrated aluminium ion.[181]

Since the fully hydrated aluminium ion has a triple positive charge, while the purpurine ion brings with it a single negative charge, the complex ion as a whole has a positive charge of two.

In the practical dyeing solution, standard aluminium purpurine (p. 111), there is only one molecule of purpurine to 8 atoms of aluminium. The composition of the solution may be expressed in terms of the *mordant quotient*;[23] that is to say, the number of atoms of mordant metal in the solution, divided by the number of dye molecules. In the standard aluminium purpurine solution, then, the quotient is 8. It must therefore be supposed that the majority of the hydrated aluminium ions in the solution that are combined with purpurine at all are combined with only one ion of it.

When ionized purpurine has associated itself with aluminium in the way indicated on p. 113, a new ring has been formed, consisting of 6 atoms arranged in the following order: aluminium, oxygen, carbon, carbon, carbon, oxygen. This ring is particularly stable. Since the purpurine sends out two bonds that grip the aluminium like the chela of a lobster, the compound is said to be chelate.[132]

Since the aluminium-purpurine ion in the dye-solution is positively charged, it will tend to combine with basiphil (negatively charged) tissue-constituents, such as the nucleic acids. It will not tend to combine with acidophil (positively charged) constituents, such as the haemoglobin of red blood-corpuscles.

It might be thought that the hydrated aluminium ion, carrying a triple positive charge, would have a greater tendency to be attracted to sites of negative charge in the tissues than would the doubly charged aluminium-purpurine ion. If so, little dyeing would be likely to occur; yet the solution dyes strongly. The explanation appears to be as follows. When some of the water molecules of a coordination complex, such as the hydrated aluminium ion, are replaced by other molecules, the solubility of the complex in water is reduced. This reduction in solubility will favour the deposition of the aluminium-purpurine ion on the sites of negative charge, while the hydrated aluminium ion has a strong tendency to remain dissolved.[181]

A few of the hydrated aluminium ions are likely to take up two purpurine ions; some may take up three. The result will be a reduction of the positive charge respectively to one or nought; in the latter case there would be precipitation of an insoluble pigment. On the analogy of the compound of purpurine with cobalt,[131] it must be regarded as probable that one aluminium atom can accept chelate bonds from three molecules of purpurine. This, however, is not certain. A great deal of study has been devoted to the attempt to discover the exact composition of the flaming red dye, Turkey red, which has been known in the East for many hundreds of years. It appears certain that although this substance contains calcium, yet the chelate bonds are all with aluminium, and that only *two* alizarine molecules are thus joined to each aluminium atom: of the two remaining covalencies of this metal, one still retains a water molecule (and the other is linked through oxygen to calcium).[75]

Compounds between mordants and dyes are known as *lakes*. The artists' water colour, madder lake, is of this nature. This insoluble substance is similar in composition to Turkey red. It is distributed by the artist's brush in the form of a fine suspension. When a mordant and a dye are dissolved together, a lake may

remain in solution, but there is often a tendency towards general
precipitation of an insoluble lake, in which the mordant metal has
combined with the maximum number of dye ions.

Although electrostatic attraction presumably draws the aluminium-purpurine ions towards sites of negative charge in the
tissues, yet a bond other than the ionic must eventually be established, for otherwise the mordant/dye complex would be no more
tightly held to the tissues than basic dyes are, and like the latter it
would be washed away readily enough by neutral ethanol. It is
probable that covalent linkages are established between the
aluminium atom and acid groups in the tissues, such as the phosphoric group of the nucleic acids. If so, the tissue/mordant/dye
complex would have the structure shown here. It will be noticed

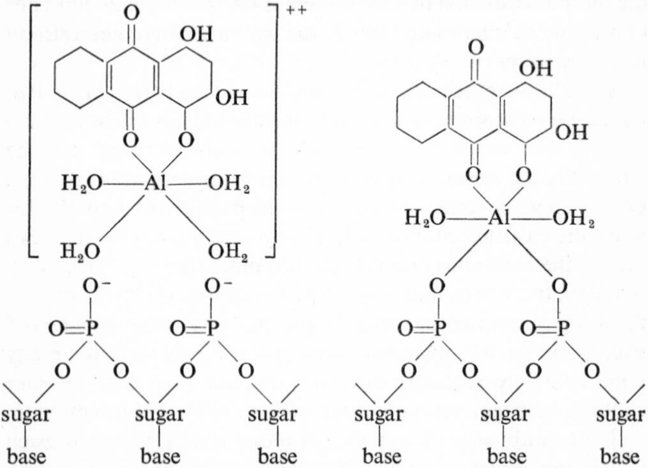

The mordant/dye complex attracted to   *The tissue/mordant/dye*
a site of negative charges (a nucleic acid)   *complex*
in the tissue

Structural formulae showing hypothetically how purpurine
may be linked to nucleic acid through aluminium

that two water molecules are freed from association with aluminium, and that the double positive charge on the mordant/dye
complex is cancelled by two negative charges on the acid.

Similar linkages are likely to be formed with carboxyl and other acid groups in proteins and other tissue-constituents.

It is not always necessary to prepare a mordant/dye complex first and subsequently to allow it to come into contact with the tissues. On the contrary, one may first soak the tissues in a solution of the mordant and then in a solution of the dye. The basiphil tissue-constituents will take up the positively charged hydrated aluminium ion and the dye will displace water from the attached aluminium complex when given the chance to do so. It might, indeed, be said that the dye is being used as a reagent for the detection of aluminium (though one might be misled if the tissues happened to contain another metal capable of mordanting the dye). Both the single-bath method (in which the dye is mixed with the mordant) and the two-bath method (in which the tissue is put first in the mordant and then in the dye) are of common use in microtechnique.

When the single-bath method is used, one may dye either regressively or progressively, but regressive dyeing is almost invariable with the two-bath process. There are two chief ways of differentiating mordant dyes after deliberate over-dyeing. One may extract the excess of dye by placing the tissue either in an acid (often a weak solution of hydrochloric acid) or else in a solution of the substance that was used to mordant.

Acids attack both the links in the tissue/mordant/dye complex. It is easy to prove that they attack the tissue/mordant link.[24] Haematein (p. 94) is a convenient dye for experiments of this kind. It is only necessary to take two slides, treat both of them with the mordant, then one only with an acid, and finally, after washing away the acid, to put both slides in the dye for the same length of time. The section that has been in the acid will be more feebly dyed than the other, because the acid has removed part of the aluminium from the tissues (and would remove it all if given sufficient time). The hydrogen ions of the acid compete with the positively charged water/aluminium complex for attachment to the negatively charged sites in the tissue.

That acids also attack the mordant/dye link is very easily shown with those dyes that change their colour when they associate with a mordant. Haematein is an example. This has a dirty red-dish colour when dissolved in water, but becomes clear blue in the presence of the aluminium ion. The addition of acid restores the original colour. Purpurine does not change colour markedly when it associates with aluminium (though alizarine changes from yellow to scarlet).

It always surprises students to learn that the mordant—the very substance that attaches the dye to the tissue—can also be used to remove the dye from it. The fact is that everything depends on the relative abundance of mordant and dye. When a section has been dyed, the total amount of dye in it is very small. If the section is now placed in a solution of the mordant, the latter is present in enormous excess. The dissolved aluminium competes with the attached aluminium for the minute amount of purpurine that is colouring the tissue. The dye redistributes itself. If sufficient time be allowed, no visible trace of dye will remain in the tissue. In practice one looks at the section under the microscope from time to time. When the objects that it is desired to show clearly are still strongly coloured, but the surrounding parts of the tissue have become colourless or scarcely tinged, one washes away the differentiating fluid with water.

While the dye is being extracted by the mordant, coloured clouds may be seen in the solution surrounding the section. Thus the solution *extracts* the dye, though both mordant and dye are present in it. It follows that whether a mordant/dye solution dyes or extracts depends on the relative abundance of dye and mordant; that is to say, on the mordanting quotient. For any particular mordant and dye one can find a concentration of each that neither increases nor decreases the intensity of colouring of tissue-constituents that have already been dyed by the same mordant and dye.[23] In experiments of this sort it is best to work with sections that have been exposed to the standard aluminium purpurine solution (p. 111) until chromatin has been strongly coloured but cytoplasm only feebly. The mordanting quotient of an aluminium purpurine solution that neither increases nor decreases the intensity of colouring of such a section is called the *critical mordant quotient*.[23] If the quotient of a solution is lower than the critical figure, the solution acts as a dye; if higher, as a differentiating agent. In the case of aluminium purpurine, with the aluminium salt dissolved at M/40 in 60% ethanol, the critical quotient is 16.

If an *undyed* section be placed in an aluminium purpurine solution in which the mordanting quotient is at the critical figure, dyeing will take place very slowly until chromatin is strongly and cytoplasm feebly coloured; no further increase of colour will occur, however long the section may remain in the dye.[23]

Solutions in which the mordanting quotient is not very many times less than the critical figure are particularly easy to use, because there is not much tendency to over-dye. Standard aluminium purpurine ('purpural'), with a mordanting quotient of 8, is an example. It can be recommended to beginners as a routine dye for chromatin and other negatively charged tissue constituents. It is to be used progressively. The period of dyeing varies according to the fixative used, but half-an-hour or an hour usually suffices. The section is then simply washed in 50% or 70% ethanol.

Haematein reacts with aluminium salts in much the same way as purpurine. As the formula on p. 94 shows, it possesses an $=O$ and a phenolic $-OH$, so situated in relation to one another as to provide means of chelation with mordants.

The mordants commonly used with haematein in microtechnique are potassium alum, $Al_2(SO_4)_3.K_2SO_2.24H_2O$, and ammonium alum, $Al_2(SO_4)_3.(NH_4)_2SO_4.24H_2O$. The colour of aluminium haematein is always blue, whatever salt of aluminium is used. The potassium and ammonium sulphates contained in these alums play no part in lake-formation, but they may affect the pH of dye solutions and the solubility of dyes. The double salts are easily crystallized and therefore easily purified. It was probably for this reason that potassium alum was used when mordant dyeing was invented in Turkey many centuries ago. The traditional use of alums persists in microtechnique to the present day, but there is no rigorous proof that alums are preferable to simple salts of aluminium.

Dye solutions are usually made with haematoxylin instead of haematein. It will be remembered that the former, if pure, is colourless (p. 94). It has the advantage of being more soluble than haematein in water and in aqueous alcoholic solutions. Gradual oxidation by atmospheric oxygen keeps up the strength of solutions for a long time. It is convenient to oxidize about a quarter or a half of the haematoxylin by sodium iodate when making up a solution, and to allow the rest to remain as a reserve.[25] Solutions made in this way are ready for immediate use and last a long time. The reserve is gradually oxidized.

Two of the most useful solutions containing aluminium haematein are Delafield's and Ehrlich's. They are called haematoxylin solutions, because it was intended by their inventors that they should be made up with the unoxidized substance, reliance being placed on atmospheric oxygen for gradual production of the dye.

In Delafield's haematoxylin[152] the mordant is ammonium alum. Glycerol and methanol act as solvents, disinfectants, and restrainers. The stock solution may be diluted as desired with distilled water. It is necessary to put the tissue in alkaline tap-water or weak ammonia solution after soaking it in the mordant/dye solution, for the alum is rather strongly acid and this prevents lake-formation. The tissue changes in colour from dirty red to clear blue, and the basiphil objects are then clearly revealed. This is an excellent dye when used progressively by experienced workers, but it is perhaps rather too quick in action for the beginner. It is suitable for whole mounts as well as sections.

In Ehrlich's haematoxylin[72] the mordant is potassium alum. Glycerol is contained in this solution, as in Delafield's, but ethanol takes the place of methanol. The chief difference from Delafield's is that acetic acid is added to prevent the formation of an insoluble lake. As a result the solution keeps almost indefinitely, and this is its great virtue. Dyeing takes much longer than with Delafield's. Ehrlich himself worked progressively, but it is usual to over-dye and extract the excess with weak aqueous hydrochloric acid. 'Blueing' by an alkaline solution is necessary.

Ferric iron is a valuable mordant for haematein. Simple ferric salts work well, but iron alum, $Fe_2(SO_4)_3.(NH_4)_2SO_4.24H_2O$, is generally used. The ferric lake is black or blue-black. It attaches itself more securely to the tissues than the aluminium lake does, and is less easily removed by acids. It does not act simply as a basic dye, but attaches itself also to certain objects that are not basiphil: in particular, to mitochondria, centrioles, and certain kinds of lipid droplets. It is probable that a covalent link is established between the iron-haematein complex and the tissue.[185] The difference between this link and that formed by the aluminium haematein complex has not been satisfactorily explained.

When ferric salts and haematein are dissolved together, an insoluble lake tends to be deposited. For this reason the two-bath method is generally used. The section is first soaked in iron alum or some other ferric salt and then transferred to a simple solution of 'ripened' (partly oxidized) haematoxylin. The latter is usually dissolved in ethanol, in which it is very soluble, and the solution subsequently diluted with water. The regressive method is used. The excess of the dye is removed by soaking the section a second time in the mordant.

Heidenhain's method[93, 94, 95] is the best-known example of this way of using iron haematein. Experienced workers can get precisely the result they require, but beginners find the differentiation rather difficult, because the extraction by the mordant seems to go faster and faster towards the end, just when one would like it to go slowly. Heidenhain's is one of the most important of all methods of dyeing in microtechnique. Almost everything in the cell can be revealed by careful differentiation, if the tissue was appropriately fixed. The black or blue-black colour gives excellent images in the microscope and is very convenient for photomicrography. Preparations are permanent in hydrophobe mounting media (p. 125), even in those (such as Canada balsam) that tend to bleach certain dyes. It is generally best not to use an acid dye in addition, because the contrast between black objects and their surroundings is necessarily reduced by any background colour.

It will be remembered that carminic acid, like purpurine, is an anthraquinonoid dye. It possesses an $=O$ and a phenolic $-OH$ placed in the same relation to each other as in purpurine. It behaves towards mordants very much like the latter dye. Its colour (crimson) does not undergo much change when it links itself to aluminium, the mordant most commonly used.

One of the best solutions is Mayer's carmalum,[118] which contains carminic acid, potassium alum, and water, with thymol, salicylic acid, or sodium salicylate as disinfectant. It is suitable for use with both sections and whole mounts. It may be used either progressively or regressively. Potassium alum (5% aqueous) readily extracts any excess of colour. This is a very easy dye to use, since it lends itself to leisurely progressive colouring. The colour is well maintained in both hydrophil and hydrophobe mounting media.

CHAPTER 10

Mounting

A mounting medium is a substance in which tissues are immersed for examination under the microscope. The same name should not be applied to adhesives that merely stick sections to slides and do not enclose the tissues at the moment of examination. Mounting is necessarily the last process to which tissues are subjected in the making of a microscopical preparation.

Solid, unshrinkable objects may be mounted dry. If so, air is to be regarded as the mounting medium. In electron-microscopy sections are examined dry, in a vacuum; if the embedding medium has been removed, the tissue constituents are exposed directly to the electron beam. With these exceptions, tissues are always mounted in media that are fluid at the outset, though many solidify later. The liquid may be a single pure substance, a mixture of liquids, or a solution of one or more solids in a liquid; it must be optically homogeneous and stable. Volatility is allowable, because the edge of the mount can be sealed (p. 133). The mounting medium must fill even the minutest spaces formed within cells by coagulant fixatives, for otherwise different parts of the specimen would be permeated by fluids of different refractive indices, and the image would therefore be confused (see fig. 4, p. 26). The mounting medium must be transparent and nearly or quite colourless. It must be capable of wetting the various tissue-constituents, especially proteins (that is to say, it must be able to lie against them without leaving any intervening spaces). It must not dissolve or corrode the tissue-constituents that are to be studied, though solvents of particular constituents (such as lipids) are permissible if the intention is to study the insoluble remainder of the tissue. It must not support the growth of moulds or bacteria.

123

The refractive index of the medium must be related to the means adopted to obtain contrast in the image produced by the microscope. An example will make this clear. Let us imagine that a piece of tissue has been fixed by formaldehyde, and that all lipids, carbohydrates, and nucleic acids have been dissolved out of it. The specimen will consist mainly of protein, and this, in its fixed condition, will generally have a refractive index of about 1·536.[69] If the fixed tissue is now thoroughly permeated by a colourless, transparent fluid of the same or very nearly the same refractive index, such as methyl salicylate,[87] the whole object disappears and no image of it can be obtained by the microscope.

A fluid that has this effect is often called a 'clearing agent', but the term is misleading. The fixed proteins of the tissue are transparent and colourless, and require no clearing. To render the tissue as a whole transparent, it is only necessary to fill all the spaces intervening between the proteins with a transparent, colourless fluid of the same refractive index. There is then no diffraction of light at the surfaces of the protein, and therefore no image of it can be formed. The protein is unaffected. Methyl salicylate no more 'clears' the proteins than a transparent, colourless fluid of the same refractive index as glass 'clears' a glass object immersed in it.

To produce contrast and thus prevent invisibility caused in the way just described, one may dye the tissue and then mount in the same medium as before. The object becomes visible because light of certain wave-lengths is reduced in intensity by the dye attached to the proteins, but passes freely through the mounting medium. The fact that the latter has the same refractive index as the proteins is now helpful, because the complete homogeneity of protein and medium in this respect is favourable to the production of an optically perfect image.

Alternatively one may leave the object undyed, but render it visible by mounting it in a fluid that differs slightly from the proteins in refractive index. The specimen should then be examined by phase-contrast microscopy. To get the best effect, the difference in refractive indices should be small. The retardation or advancement of the light that passes through the object in relation to that which passes only through the mounting medium should not greatly exceed a quarter of a wave-length of the light used for examination, if phase-contrast is to be applied effectively.[27]

A transparent object is rendered visible by direct[17] ('ordinary') microscopy if it is mounted in a medium of much lower or higher refractive index than its own. This is convenient if nothing more is needed than a low-power view of a whole mount; but wherever the object comes up against the medium there will necessarily be a Becke line[159, 92] in the microscopical image, and this is a misleading appearance, since it does not represent anything that was present in the object. The resolution of minute detail is not possible in such circumstances.

Mounting media may be classified as hydrophil and hydrophobe. The hydrophil media are those that contain water or are miscible with water. Sections or whole mounts may be transferred from water to hydrophil media without the necessity to use an intermediary liquid not contained in the medium. It is reasonable, however, to introduce the mounting medium gradually to the tissue. Thus, in mounting in glycerol (p. 128) or Farrants's medium one may pass the section or other object through a mixture of water and glycerol before mounting in the medium itself. The two substances may conveniently be mixed in the proportion in which they occur in Farrants's medium (50 g = 41·7 ml of glycerol with 100 ml of distilled water).

Hydrophobe media require the dehydration of the object, since they are not miscible with water. It is usual to pass tissues through a graded series of ethanols (often 70%, 90%, absolute). Tissues that have been dehydrated by ethanol in the course of embedding have undergone all the shrinkage of which they are capable, and no harm could come from direct passage of sections from water to absolute ethanol. However, the absolute ethanol would soon be diluted if this were done repeatedly, and similarly the 90% ethanol would soon lose its strength if direct passage were made from water to ethanol of this concentration. The closer the grading of the ethanols, the more accurately they will maintain their concentration, but the more trouble will be involved in dehydration. The usual series provides a good compromise. The dehydrated section is usually transferred to the solvent contained in the mounting medium, and from this to the mounting medium itself. Some hydrophobe media, however, contain no solvent. Methyl salicylate is an example. The tissue is transferred directly from absolute ethanol to such media.

Both hydrophil and hydrophobe mounting media are further subdivisible into those that are adhesive (and thus bind the coverslip to the slide) and those that are not. If a preparation is to be kept permanently, it is almost essential that the coverslip should be bound to the slide. The easiest way of achieving this is to use an adhesive mounting medium.

If perfect apposition can be obtained between two solid objects, they will ordinarily adhere, because their molecules will be drawn towards one another by the same forces that hold the molecules together in the objects themselves.[42] There is no question, however, of causing coverslip and slide to adhere in this way, partly because their surfaces cannot be made flat enough for perfect apposition on the molecular scale, partly because a section or other microscopical object must necessarily intervene. Some degree of adhesion will be achieved if a fluid intervenes, provided that the fluid is able to wet both the surfaces concerned.[46] It is a fortunate circumstance that glass can be wetted both by water and by the solvents used in hydrophobe mounting media. The adhesion will be very poor, however, unless the liquid not only adheres to the glass but also coheres within itself. In other words, it must be viscous, or else be capable of actual conversion into a solid. The presence of long molecules in the liquid will thus favour adhesion. So that the surfaces may be easily wetted, it is desirable that the adhesive should be at first of fairly low viscosity. The necessary increase in viscosity or conversion to solid may be achieved either by cooling or by the evaporation of a solvent.

The adhesive hydrophobe mounting media, such as DPX (p. 131), are hardened by evaporation of the solvent, which is usually xylene. The commercial product that is sold under this name is a mixture of three isomeric dimethyl benzenes with ethyl

benzene. It has the percentage composition shown here, whether

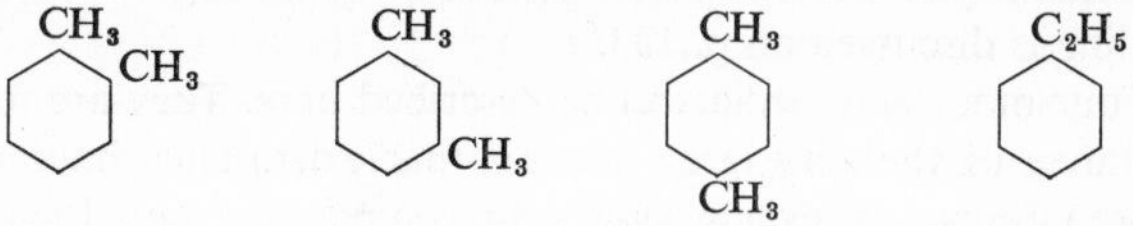

CH$_3$ CH$_3$ / CH$_3$ CH$_3$ C$_2$H$_5$ (chemical structures)

o-*xylene*, 23%   m-*xylene*, 43%   p-*xylene*, 19%   *ethyl benzene*, 15%

The components of xylene

it is derived from petroleum or coal.[102] Xylene is chosen as a solvent for hydrophobe mounting media because it evaporates sufficiently slowly to allow the coverslip to be adjusted at leisure. Hardening is usually hastened by putting the slide on a warm plate after the coverslip has been arranged in position.

Hydrophil media are used when low refractive indices are required, or when it is desired to avoid dehydration at all stages. Most hydrophobe media have high or rather high indices, approximating to those of proteins that have been fixed by formaldehyde or by coagulant fixatives. These hydrophobe media generally give more transparent preparations than hydrophil ones.

Non-adhesive media present the advantage that the final refractive index is known, because there is (or should be) no loss of a particular component (or components) by evaporation.

One cannot state the effective refractive indices of those adhesive media that rely for adhesion on the evaporation of a volatile component, because the exact amount of this component (if any) that remains in the preparation at any particular time cannot be controlled. One can only state the extreme limits of refractive index: that is to say, the index of the complete medium, ready for use, and the index of the medium from which the volatile component has been completely driven off. It is unlikely that this component is quite eliminated from ordinary microscopical preparations.

Since high refractive index and firm adhesion of the coverslip are desirable in most cases, adhesive hydrophobe media are more often used than the others.

When non-adhesive media are used, it is generally desirable to

stick the coverslip to the slide by the use of a seal, which prevents movement and also the evaporation of any volatile constituent. Sealing is discussed on p. 133.

Four mounting media will be described here. They are representative of the very large number that exist. They have been chosen because they are simple in composition and therefore demonstrate well the principles involved in the process of mounting. The selected examples are these:

hydrophil
    non-adhesive (fluid mount)   . glycerol (see below)
    adhesive   .   .   . Farrants's medium (p. 129)
hydrophobe
    non-adhesive (fluid mount)   . methyl salicylate (p. 130)
    adhesive   .   .   . DPX (p. 131)

Glycerol (glycerine) is a familiar non-adhesive hydrophil medium. It is useful in studies of lipids, which are preserved whether fixed or not. Lysochromes (p. 86) maintain their colour well in this medium, but certain dyes, including mordanted haematein, are not perfectly stable.[148] Glycerol is very valuable as a mounting medium for sections of tissues that have been embedded in butyl methacrylate and are intended for study, without dyeing, by phase-contrast microscopy.[24] When preparing tissues for electron-microscopy it is desirable to cut a few sections at about 3 μ and to examine these by phase-contrast. This shows at once whether the tissue is well enough fixed to make it worth while to cut thin sections and mount them on grids for electron-microscopy. It also helps in the interpretation of electron-micrographs, because the thickness of the section enables one to focus up and down and thus obtain a three-dimensional view. Material that has been fixed in Palade (p. 58), embedded in methacrylate (p. 77), sectioned at about 3 μ, and mounted in diluted glycerol, gives an extraordinarily lifelike appearance under the microscope. A few authors[138, 176] have studied methacrylate sections by phase-contrast, but not nearly enough has been done in this promising field.

It is generally supposed that the fixed proteins of the cell have

a refractive index of about 1·535. This supposition rests on observations made with tissues fixed in formaldehyde solution and embedded in paraffin.[69] There is reason to believe that the proteins of cells that have been fixed by osmium tetroxide and embedded in butyl methacrylate have a considerably lower index than this. It is desirable that the index of the mounting medium should be somewhat lower again, if undyed sections are to be examined by phase-contrast. The ground cytoplasm will then appear very pale grey by positive contrast, while the mitochondria and certain other cytoplasmic inclusions will be dark grey or black. A mounting medium of refractive index 1·46 has been recommended.[138] Media with even lower indices, such as 1·44 or 1·42, seem to give still better results.[24] The refractive index of pure glycerol is 1·474. By mixture with water, any lower refractive index exceeding that of water itself (1·333) can be obtained. The proportions of glycerol and water that give various refractive indices are shown in published tables.[127] To make a fluid of index 1·44, 78 g of glycerol are mixed with 22 ml of distilled water; of index 1·42, 65 g of glycerol with 35 ml of water.

By the addition of cadmium chloride, the refractive index of glycerol may be increased to 1·54 at saturation.[148] The salt imparts a pale yellow tint to this otherwise colourless medium.

Farrants's medium is a good example of an adhesive, hydrophil medium, much used in studies of lipids. It is not nearly so good as diluted glycerine for the study of undyed methacrylate sections by phase-contrast.

Several different formulae have been published, all containing the same three principal ingredients. The following[29] works well.

To 40 g of gum arabic (preferably powdered), add 40 ml of distilled water. When the gum has dissolved, add 20 g of glycerol. A piece of camphor may be put in the medium to act as a disinfectant.

The pH of this fluid is 4·1, whether camphor be added or not.[24]

True gums are sticky, water-soluble substances that exude through cracks in the bark of certain trees. Gum arabic (acacia gum) is derived from species of *Acacia* (Leguminosae), especially *A. senegal*, a native of the Sudan and other parts of tropical

K

Africa. The gum is taken from both wild and cultivated trees.[4] Its name refers to the fact that it was first imported into Europe from Arabian ports. The gum consists of the calcium salt of arabic acid,[102] which owes its acidity to the carboxyl group of glucuronic acid. Hydrolysis yields arabinose, rhamnose, and

arabinose   *rhamnose*   *galactose*   *glucuronic acid*

Skeleton-formulae of the hydrolytic products of gum arabic

galactose, in addition to glucuronic acid. The exact way in which these are bound together in the natural product is not known, but the evidence suggests a branched chain, in which the components are not arranged in a regularly repeated order.[122] The molecular weight is about 240,000.[102] The shape and size of the molecule determine its high viscosity in aqueous solution.

The refractive index of the medium made up according to the formula given above is 1·423 (or 1·424 if saturated with camphor).[24] It is best to drive off most of the water (and thus increase the refractive index) by leaving the slide overnight in the paraffin oven, after applying the coverslip. The latter adheres firmly.

It has been stated in print that 'The ordinary media of the Farrants' type have an index of refraction just over 1·3.' [86] This statement cannot be correct, whichever formula be followed; for the refractive index of water itself is 1·333, while those of the other constituents are very much higher.

The glycerine in Farrants's medium prevents the gum from cracking when the water is driven off. It also helps to make the tissue transparent, because it readily penetrates the minute spaces in them, while the large molecules of the gum diffuse slowly. The uneven distribution through the tissue of the two substances of high refractive index in this medium is probably the cause of the imperfection of the phase-contrast image.

Methyl salicylate.[87] Non-adhesive hydrophobe media are very seldom used, partly because most of the suitable substances are inconveniently volatile, partly because it is so easy to prepare hydrophobe media that will stick firmly to glass. Methyl salicylate, however, has certain virtues. It is colourless and miscible

Methyl salicylate

in all proportions with absolute ethanol. It gives excellent transparency to most preparations, because its refractive index (1·537) is very close to that of proteins fixed in the usual ways (see p. 124). Since it is a single substance, there is no question of change of refractive index by differential evaporation of components. Basic, acid, and mordanted dyes seem to maintain their colours well in it.

DPX.[103] It has already been remarked that adhesive hydrophobe mounting media are more commonly used than any others. They are valuable for making permanent preparations of dyed objects. Dyes maintain their colours well in DPX, which possesses the further advantage of being itself perfectly colourless. The letters DPX are the initials of Distrene-Plasticizer-Xylene.

The most familiar of all media in this group is Canada balsam, which was described in earlier editions of this book. Although it has great virtues, it is omitted from the present edition, partly because it has a tendency to bleach basic dyes, partly because it is very complex in composition (there are at least 7 constituents in addition to the solvent).[179]

In adhesive hydrophobe media the essential constituent is a 'resin', in the wide sense of that term: that is to say, a solid, amorphous organic compound, insoluble in water, having no definite melting-point (because composed of molecules of varying lengths). The natural resins that exude from the bark of certain trees are oxidation-products of terpenes, but plastics having similar physical characters nowadays receive the same name. The particular plastic that gives high refractive index and adhesiveness to DPX is polystyrene, a polymer having the same general character as acrylic acid (p. 78), but differing in the substitution of a phenyl group for the carboxyl of the acid. The polymer that is used in DPX has rather less than 800 segmers in most of its

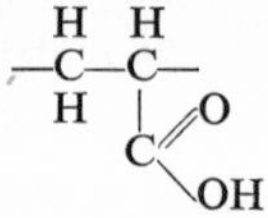

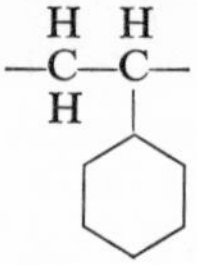

H H
—C—C—
H | C⟋O
     \OH

A segmer of acrylic acid

H H
—C—C—
H |

A segmer of polystyrene

molecules. It is known by the trade name of 'distrene 80'. It is a colourless solid, freely soluble in xylene.

If a section or other object be mounted in a solution of distrene 80 in xylene, the polymer retracts under the edges of the coverslip as the solvent evaporates. This defect is mitigated or overcome by the addition of a plasticizer to the medium. Typical plasticizers are non-volatile solvents of the plastic on which they act. They are supposed to associate themselves with reactive groups in the polymer, which would otherwise attach themselves to other reactive groups, and thus link the long molecules into a rigid meshwork; but they do not combine with the polymer so as to form a new substance. Thus they make the polymer softer than it would otherwise be, and oppose its contraction when any volatile solvent evaporates. The plasticizer in DPX is tri-*p*-tolyl phosphate (often called tricresyl phosphate); that is to say, an ester of phosphoric acid, in which three *p*-tolyl radicles have replaced three hydrogens.

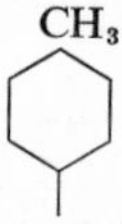

CH₃

The p-tolyl radicle

This plasticizer is a colourless, non-volatile liquid of high refractive index (about 1·56).

To prepare DPX, add to 100 ml of xylene 18·75 ml of tri-*p*-tolyl phosphate, and then 25 g of distrene 80. The latter is obtainable from Messrs Honeywill and Stein, 21 St James's Square, London, S.W.1. The plasticizer is irritating to the skin and contact should be avoided.

The refractive index of DPX, while it still contains the original amount of xylene, is 1·532. Since the index of xylene is only about 1·496, that of the medium must increase as drying proceeds. The final index is rather higher than that of the fixed proteins of ordinary microscopical preparations. If all the xylene is deliberately driven off from DPX, the resultant substance (distrene + plasticizer) is a solid, melting above 100° C.[103] Although the plasticizer is a solvent for distrene, not nearly enough of it is present to make a solution.

In whole mounts there is some tendency to retraction under the coverslip, despite the presence of the plasticizer.

Permanent preparations can be made of objects mounted in non-adhesive media, by sticking the periphery of the upper surface of the coverslip to the slide (fig. 7). The gelatine gel used for embedding (p. 70) is a good adhesive for this purpose.[24] It melts readily in an incubator at 37° C. The slide is dried with a cloth up to the edge of the coverslip, and the melted gel applied with a paint brush. It hardens at first by becoming a gel again, and subsequently by evaporation of the water. In a day or two it becomes so hard that it can scarcely be marked with the finger-nail. Both hydrophil and hydrophobe mounting media can be sealed with gelatine.

As an extra precaution against evaporation of the mounting medium, it is wise to varnish the hardened gelatine and to extend the varnish beyond the gelatine on to the upper surfaces of the coverslip and slide (fig. 7). The varnish chosen for this purpose should be one that makes perfect contact with glass surfaces and is not readily softened or dissolved by the various fluids used as immersion-oils. Gold size is convenient for the purpose. This is a substance used by gilders in the preparation of surfaces to receive gold foil. It consists essentially of an oleo-resin dissolved with turpentine and linseed oil.[180] The oleo-resin (or resin dissolved in an essential oil) is often wrongly called 'gum' animi. It exudes from the bark of a leguminous tree, *Hymenaea courbaril*, a native of the West Indies.[183] Two separate processes are involved in the drying of this varnish: first, the evaporation of the essential oils;

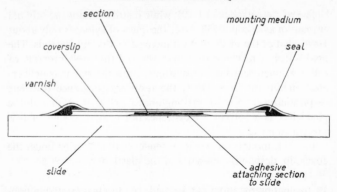

Fig. 7. Diagram of a finished microscopical slide in sectional view,
showing adhesives and varnish.

secondly, the oxidation by atmospheric oxygen of the linoleic and
other unsaturated fatty acids contained in the linseed oil. This
oxidation is helped by heating the oil with lead monoxide in the
preparation of the varnish. The hardening occupies some days
after the varnish has been applied.

All finished microscopical preparations of organisms and their
parts, other than those of living cells still lying in the fluid that
bathed them in their natural environment, are to be regarded as
products of the reaction between the living tissues and the various
media in which they have successively been soaked. The reaction-
products, which are what we study under the microscope, are only
informative about organisms and their life-processes if some
knowledge is available about the reactions involved; and this
presupposes knowledge of the reagents. It has been the purpose
of this book to supply information about the reagents that are
used in some of the simplest processes of routine microtechnique,
and about their reactions with tissue-constituents.

   If an unknown tissue or cell be acted upon by an unknown reagent, no useful information can be obtained. Cytologists and
histologists should be as loath to use secret reagents as doctors
are to use secret medicines. Quite a lot of fancifully named embed-

ding and mounting media of unstated chemical composition are in use today, despite the fact that their reactions with tissue-constituents cannot be understood while their formulae remain secret. Even the field of electron-microscopy, in which a scientific outlook might have been expected, has been invaded by makers of secret mixtures. For instance, we are asked to use 'hardeners' and 'accelerators' to solidify an embedding medium, without being told what these reagents may be. We cannot interpret the resultant electron-micrographs satisfactorily without this information, because it is necessary to know whether any tissue-constituents are likely to have been dissolved or affected in some other way. Reagents of all kinds used in microtechnique should be prepared in the biological laboratory, or obtained from reliable manufacturers who announce the composition of their products. The only possible exceptions are such substances as varnishes, which do not come into contact with the tissues.

List of References

1. Allen, E., 1916. *Anat. Rec.*, **10**, 565.
2. Altmann, R., 1889. *Arch. Anat. Physiol.*, *Anat. Abt.*, Supplement-Band, 86.
3. —— 1894. *Die Elementatorganismen und ihre Beziehungen zu den Zellen.* 2nd ed. Leipzig (Veit).
4. Anon., 1930. *Official guide to the museums of economic botany. No. 1. Dicotyledons.* London (H.M. Stationery Office).
5. Anson, M. L., 1938. Chapter on 'The coagulation of proteins' in *The chemistry of the amino-acids and proteins*, ed. by C. L. A. Schmidt. Springfield, Ill. (Thomas).
6. ——, 1945. *Adv. prot. Chem.*, **2**, 361.
7. Apàthy, S. V., 1912. *Z. wiss. Mikr.*, **29**, 449.
8. Bahr, G. D., 1954. *Exp. cell Res.*, **7**, 457.
9. Bahr, G. F., Bloom, G., & Friberg, U., 1957. Ibid., **12**, 342.
10. Baker, J. R., 1944. *Quart. J. micr. Sci.*, **85**, 1.
11. —— 1946. Ibid., **87**, 441.
12. —— 1947. Ibid., **88**, 463.
13. —— 1948. Ibid., **89**, 103.
14. —— 1949. Ibid., **90**, 293.
15. —— 1953. *Nature*, **172**, 617.
16. —— 1956. *Quart. J. micr. Sci.*, **97**, 621.
17. —— 1956. *Nature*, **177**, 194.
18. —— 1957. Ibid., **180**, 947.
19. —— 1957. *Symp. Soc. exp. Biol.*, **10**, 1.
20. —— 1958. *J. Histochem. Cytochem.*, **6**, 303.
21. —— 1958. *Principles of biological microtechnique: a study of fixation and dyeing.* London (Methuen).
22. —— 1957. *J. roy. micr. Soc.*, **77**, 116.
23. —— 1960. *Quart. J. micr. Sci.* (in the press).

24. —— Results not previously published.

25. Baker, J. R., & Jordan, B. M., 1953. *Quart. J. micr. Sci.*, **94**, 237.

26. Baker, J. R., & Luke, B. M. Results not previously published.

27. Barer, R., & Joseph, S., 1955. *Quart. J. micr. Sci.*, **96**, 423.

28. Bauer, H., 1933. *Jahrb. Morph. mikr. Anat.*, 2 Abt., **33**, 143.

29. Beale, L. S., 1880. *How to work with the microscope*. London (Harrison).

30. Bělař, K., 1928. Article on 'Die Technik der descriptiven Cytologie' in T. Peterfi's *Methodik der wissenschaftlichen Biologie*. Berlin (Springer).

31. Benda, C., 1898. *Arch. Anat. Physiol.*, physiol. Abt. (no vol. number), 393.

32. —— 1903. *Anat. Hefte*, 2 Abt., **12**, 743.

33. Bensley, R. R., & Hoerr, N. L., 1934. *Anat. Rec.*, **60**, 449.

34. Berg, W., 1927. Article on 'Osmiumsäure' in R. Krause's *Enzyklopädie der mikroskopischen Technik*, Vol. 3. Berlin (Urban & Schwarzenberg).

35. Billmeyer, F. W., 1957. *Textbook of polymer chemistry*. New York (Interscience).

36. Bird, C. L., 1951. *The theory and practice of wool dyeing*. Bradford (Society of Dyers and Colourists).

37. Böeseken, J., & Giffen, J. van, 1920. *Rec. Trav. chim. Pays-Bas*, **39**, 183.

38. Bouin, M. & P., 1898. *Bibliog. anat.*, **6**, 1.

39. Bouin, P., 1897. *Arch. d'Anat. micr.*, **1**, 225.

40. Boveri, T., 1888*a*. *Sitz. Ges. Morph. Physiol. München*, **3**, 71.

41. —— 1888*b*. *Jenaische Zeit.*, **22**, 685.

42. Bowden, F. P., 1957. *Endeavour*, **16**, 5.

43. Bradbury, S., & Meek, G. A., 1958. *J. biophys. biochem. Cytol.*, **4**, 603.

44. Brante, G., 1949. *Acta physiol. Scand.*, **18**, Suppl. 63, 1.

45. Brönsted, J. N., & Volqvartz, K., 1928. *Z. physikal. Chem.*, **134**, 97.

K*

46. Bruyne, N. A. de, 1957. *Nature*, **180**, 262.
47. Buchsbaum, R., 1948. *Anat. Rec.*, **102**, 19.
48. Carleton, H. M., & Drury, R. A. B., 1957. *Histological technique*. 3rd ed. London (Oxford University Press).
49. Carnoy, J. B., 1886. *Cellule*, **3**, 1.
50. Casselman, W. G. B., 1952. *Quart. J. micr. Sci.*, **93**, 381.
51. —— 1955a. Ibid., **96**, 203.
52. —— 1955b. Ibid., **96**, 223.
53. —— 1959. *Histochemical technique*. London (Methuen).
54. —— Personal communication.
54a. Champy, C., 1911. *Arch. d'Anat. micr.*, **13**, 55.
55. Chou, J. T. Y., 1957a. *Quart. J. micr. Sci.*, **98**, 47.
56. —— 1957b. Ibid., **98**, 59.
57. —— 1957c. Ibid., **98**, 431.
58. —— 1958a. Ibid., **99**, 229.
59. —— 1958b. Ibid., **99**, 285.
60. Chou, J. T. Y., & Meek, G., 1958. Ibid., **99**, 279.
61. Ciaccio, C., 1926. *Boll. Soc. ital. Biol. sperim.*, **1**, 47.
62. Clarke, J. L., 1851. *Phil. Trans.*, **141**, 607.
63. Clayton, B.-P., 1958. *Quart. J. micr. Sci.*, **99**, 453.
64. Collin, R., 1923. *C. r. Soc. Biol.*, **89**, 562.
65. —— 1924. Ibid., **91**, 793.
66. Crawford, G. N. C., & Barer, R., 1951. *Quart. J. micr. Sci.*, **92**, 403.
67. Criegee, R., 1936. *Liebigs Ann.*, **522**, 75.
68. Criegee, R., Marchand, B., & Wannowius, H., 1942. Ibid., **550**, 99.
69. Crossmon, G. C., 1949. *Stain Tech.*, **24**, 241.
70. d'Alelio, G. F., 1952. '*Fundamental principles of polymerization: rubbers, plastics, and fibers.*' London (Chapman & Hall).
71. Duesberg, J., 1920. *Contrib. Embryol. Carnegie Inst.*, **9**, 28.
72. Ehrlich, P., 1886. *Z. wiss. Mikr.*, **3**, 150.
73. Evans, J. F., 1949. Chapter 15 in J. M. Preston's *Fibre science*. Manchester (Textile Institute).
74. Fearon, W. R., & Foster, D. L., 1922. *Biochem. J.*, **16**, 564.

75. Fierz-David, H. E., & Rutishauser, M., 1940. *Helv. chim. Acta*, **23**, 1298.
76. Fischer, A., 1899. *Fixierung, Färbung und Bau des Protoplasmas*. Jena (Fischer).
77. Flemming, W., 1884. *Zeit. wiss. Mikr.*, **1**, 349.
78. Fraenkel-Conrat, H., Cooper, M., & Olcutt, H., 1945. *J. Amer. chem. Soc.*, **67**, 950.
79. Frey, H., 1863. *Das Mikroskop und die mikroskopische Technik*. Leipzig (Engelmann).
80. Frey-Wyssling, A., 1948. *Sub-microscopic morphology of protoplasm and its derivatives*. London (Elsevier).
81. Garnier, C., 1900. *J. Anat. Paris*, **36**, 22.
82. Gaunt, J. F., 1949. *J. Soc. Dyers & Col.*, **65**, 429.
83. Giles, C. H., 1944. Ibid., **60**, 303.
84. Gilev, V. P., 1958. *J. ultrastr. Res.*, **1**, 349.
85. Gray, P., 1952. *Handbook of basic microtechnique*. London (Constable).
86. —— 1954. *The microtomist's formulary and guide*. London (Constable).
87. Guéguen, F., 1898. *C. r. Soc. Biol.*, **50**, 285.
88. Gustavson, K. H., 1956. *The chemistry and reactivity of collagen*. New York (Academic Press).
88a. Haarmann, W., 1943. *Biochem. Zeit.*, **314**, 1.
89. Haeckel, E., 1866. *Generelle Morphologie der Organismen*. Vol. 1. Berlin (Reimer).
90. Hammar, J. A., 1924. *Z. mikr. Anat. Forsch.*, **1**, 85.
91. Harris, J. E., 1939. *J. exp. Biol.*, **16**, 258.
92. Hartshorne, N. H., & Stuart, A., 1950. *Crystals and the polarizing microscope*. 2nd ed. London (Arnold).
93. Heidenhain, M., 1892. *Festschrift für Kölliker*, p. 109.
94. —— 1894. *Arch. mikr. Anat.*, **43**, 423.
95. —— 1896. *Z. wiss. Mikr.*, **13**, 186.
96. —— 1916. Ibid., **33**, 232.
97. Helly, K., 1903. Ibid., **20**, 413.
98. Hermann, F., 1889. *Arch. mikr. Anat.*, **34**, 58.
99. Hertwig, G., 1931. *Zeit. mikr.-anat. Forsch.*, **23**, 484.
100. Hibbard, H., 1945. *Quart. Rev. Biol.*, **20**, 1.

101. Kimmelstiel, P., 1929. *Z. physiol. Chem.*, **184**, 143.

102. Kirk, R. E., & Othmer, D. F., 1947–55. *Encyclopaedia of chemical technology.* 14 vols. New York (Interscience).

103. Kirkpatrick, J., & Lendrum, A. C., 1939. *J. Path. Bact.*, **49**, 592.

104. Kramer, H., & Windrum, G. M., 1955. *J. Histochem. Cytochem.*, **3**, 227.

105. Langeron, M., 1949. *Précis de microscopie.* 7th ed. Paris (Masson).

106. Lassek, A. M., 1950. *Anat. Rec.*, **107**, 409.

107. Latta, H., & Hartmann, J. F., 1950. *Proc. Soc. exp. Biol. Med.*, **74**, 436.

108. Leathes, J. B., 1925. *Lancet*, **1**, 957.

109. Lewitsky, G., 1911. *Ber. deut. bot. Ges.*, **29**, 685.

110. Lison, L., 1935. *Arch. Biol.*, **46**, 599.

111. —— 1953. *Histochimie et cytochimie animales: principes et méthodes.* Paris (Gauthier-Villars).

112. MacLennan, R. F., 1941. Chapter on 'Cytoplasmic inclusions in Protozoa in biological research', ed. by G. N. Calkins & F. M. Summers. New York (Columbia University Press).

113. Malhotra, S. K., 1959. *Quart. J. micr. Sci.*, **100**, 339.

114. Mallory, F. B., 1900. *J. exp. Med.*, **5**, 15.

115. Mann, G., 1894. *Z. wiss. Mikr.*, **11**, 479.

116. —— 1902. *Physiological histology.* Oxford (Clarendon Press).

117. Mayer, P., 1883. *Mitt. zool. Stat. Neapel*, **4**, 521.

118. —— 1892. Ibid., **10**, 489.

119. —— 1918. *Zeit. wiss. Mikr.*, **35**, 161.

120. Medawar, P. B., 1941. *J. roy. micr. Soc.*, **61**, 46.

121. Meves, F., 1896. *Anat. Hefte*, 2 Abt., **6**, 284.

122. Meyer, K. H., 1950. *Natural and synthetic high polymers.* New York (Interscience).

123. Michaelis, L., 1931. *Biochem. Zeit.*, **234**, 139.

124. —— 1947. *Cold Spring Harb. Symp. quant. Biol.*, **12**, 131.

125. Michaelis, L., & Granick, S., 1945. *J. Amer. chem. Soc.*, **67**, 1212.

126. Millot, J., & Giberton, A., 1927. *C. r. Soc. Biol.*, **97**, 1674.

127. Miner, C. S., & Dalton, N. N., edited by, 1953. *Glycerol.* New York (Reinhold).

128. Mladenovic, M., & Lieb, H., 1929. *Z. physiol. Chem.*, **181**, 221.

129. Mohl, H. v., 1846. *Bot. Zeit.*, **4**, col. 73.

130. Möllendorff, W. v., 1924. *Ergebn. Anat. Entw.*, **25**, 1.

131. Morgan, G. T., & Smith, J. D. M., 1922. *Trans. chem. Soc.*, **121**, 160.

132. Morgan, G. T., & Smith, J. D. M., 1925. *J. Soc. Dyers & Col.*, **41**, 233.

133. Nath, V., 1957. *Nature*, **180**, 967.

134. Neale, S. M., 1947. *J. Soc. Dyers & Col.*, **63**, 368.

135. Nedzel, G. A., 1951. *Quart. J. micr. Sci.*, **92**, 343.

136. Neurath, H., Greenstein, J. P., Putnam, F. W., & Erickson, J. O., 1944. *Chem. Rev.*, **34**, 157.

137. Newman, S. B., Borysko, E., & Swerdlow, M., 1949. *Science*, **110**, 66.

138. Ornstein, L., & Pollister, A. W., 1952. *Trans. New York Acad. Sci.*, **14**, 194.

139. Palade, G. E., 1952. *J. exp. Med.*, **95**, 285.

140. —— 1955. *J. biophys. biochem. Cytol.*, **1**, 59.

141. Palade, G. E., & Porter, K. R., 1954. *J. exp. Med.*, **100**, 641.

142. Palay, S. L., & Palade, G. E., 1955. *J. biophys. biochem. Cytol.*, **1**, 69.

143. Pantin, C. F. A., 1946. *Notes on microscopical technique for zoologists.* Cambridge (University Press).

144. Pasteels, J. J., 1954. *Symposium on fine structure of cells*, at 8th Congress of Society for Cell Biology, Leiden.

145. Petrunkevitch, A., & Pickford, G. E., 1936. *Anat. Rec.*, **65**, 461.

146. Pischinger, A., 1926. *Zeit. Zellforsch. mikr. Anat.*, **26**, 249.

147. Policard, A., Bessis, M., & Bricka, M., 1952. *Bull. Micr. appl.*, **2**, 29.

148. Policard, A., Bessis, M., and Locquin, M., 1957. *Traité de microscopie.* Paris (Masson).

149. Porter, K. R., 1953. *J. exp. Med.*, **97**, 727.

150. Porter, K. R., & Kallman, F., 1953. *Exp. cell Res.*, **4**, 127.

151. Porter, K. R., & Thompson, H. P., 1947. *Cancer Res.*, **7**, 431.

152. Prudden, J. M., 1885. *Z. wiss. Mikr.*, **2**, 288.

153. Purkinje, J., 1840. *Uebers. Arb. Veränd. schles. Ges. vat. Kult.*, **16**, 81.

154. Putnam, F. W., 1953. Chapter on 'Protein denaturation' in *The proteins: chemistry, biological activity, and methods*, Vol. 1, Part B. New York (Academic Press).

155. Race, E., Rowe, F. M., & Speakman, J. B., 1946. *J. Soc. Dyers & Col.*, **62**, 372.

156. Regaud, C., 1910. *Arch. d'Anat. micr.*, **11**, 291.

157. Revel, J. P., Ito, S., & Fawcett, E. W., 1958. *J. biophys. biochem. Cytol.*, **4**, 495.

158. Riddle, E. H., 1954. *Monomeric acrylic esters*. New York (Reinhold).

159. Rogers, A. F., 1937. *Introduction to the study of minerals*. New York (McGraw-Hill).

160. Romeis, B., 1928. *Taschenbuch der mikroskopischen Technik*. München (Oldenbourg).

161. —— 1948. *Mikroskopische Technik*. München (Leibniz).

162. Ross, K. F. A., 1953. *Quart. J. micr. Sci.*, **94**, 125.

163. —— 1954a. *Nature*, **174**, 836.

164. —— 1954b. *Quart. J. micr. Sci.*, **95**, 425.

165. Ross, K. F. A., & Chou, J. T. Y., 1957. Ibid., **98**, 341.

166. Sanfelice, F., 1918. *Ann. Inst. Pasteur*, **32**, 363.

167. Schlottke, E., 1931. *Z. mikr.-anat. Forsch.*, **24**, 101.

168. Seki, M., 1932. *Fol. anat. Jap.*, **10**, 621.

169. —— 1936. *Zeit. Zellforsch. mikr. Anat.*, **24**, 186.

170. Shafiq, S. A., 1953a. *Quart. J. micr. Sci.*, **94**, 319.

171. —— 1953b. Ibid., **95**, 305.

172. Sidgwick, N. V., 1942. *The electronic theory of valency*. London (Oxford University Press).

173. —— 1950. *The chemical elements and their compounds*. 2 vols. Oxford (Clarendon Press).

174. Smith, J. L., & Mair, W., 1908. *J. Path. Bact.*, **12**, 134.

175. Starke, J., 1895. *Arch. Anat. Physiol.*, *physiol. Abt.* (no vol. number), 70.

176. Stoeckenius, W., 1957. *Zeit. wiss. Mikr.*, **63**, 210.

177. Strangeways, T. S. P., & Canti, R. G., 1927. *Quart J. micr. Sci.*, **71**, 1.

178. Sylvén, B., 1951. Ibid., **95**, 327.

179. Tschirch, A., & Brüning, E., 1900. *Arch. der Pharm.*, **238**, 487.

180. Tweney, C. F., & Shirshov, I. P., *n.d. Hutchinson's technical and scientific encyclopaedia.* 4 vols. London (Hutchinson).

181. Venanzi, L. M. Personal communication.

182. Virchow, H., 1885. *Arch. mikr. Anat.*, **24**, 117.

183. Wehmer, C., 1929. '*Die Pflanzenstoffe.*' 2nd ed. 2 vols. Jena (Fischer).

184. Weil, A., 1929. *J. biol. Chem.*, **83**, 601.

185. Wigglesworth, V. B., 1952. *Quart J. micr. Sci.*, **93**, 105.

186. Wolman, M., & Greco, J., 1952. *Stain Tech.*, **27**, 317.

186a Yost, D. M., & White, R. J., 1928. *J. Amer. chem. Soc.* **50** ,81.

187. Young, J. Z., 1935. *Nature*, **135**, 823.

188. Zenker, K., 1894. *Münch. med. Woch.*, **41**, 532.

189. Zirkle, C., 1928*a. Protoplasma*, **4**, 201.

190. —— 1928*b.* Ibid., **5**, 511.

Index

Where two or more consecutive pages are entirely devoted to the same subject, only the first is mentioned in the Index.

Each reference to a particular subject that is distinctly more important than other references to the same subject, is distinguished by the printing of the page-number in heavy type.